D1264175

U.S. on the Moon
What it means to us

U.S. on the Moon
What it means to us

BOOKS by U.S.NEWS & WORLD REPORT
A division of U.S.News & World Report, Inc.

WASHINGTON, D.C.

1969

Contents

Contents

Acknowledgments

Material for *U.S. on the Moon* was gathered first-hand from a number of authoritative sources in many parts of the country. They include officials, scientists, and other members of the National Aeronautics and Space Administration at headquarters in Washington, D.C.; at the Goddard Space Flight Center, Greenbelt, Maryland; at the Jet Propulsion Laboratory, Pasadena, California; at the John F. Kennedy Space Center, Florida; and at the Manned Spacecraft Center, Houston, Texas.

Material for the text and for illustrations also was obtained from a number of primary contractors of Project Apollo, including the North American Rockwell Corporation (spacecraft command and service modules and engines for the Saturn 5 rocket); Grumman Aircraft Engineering Corporation (lunar module); General Electric (Apollo checkout and reliability); the Boeing Company (technical integration and evaluation, first stage of Saturn 5, Saturn 5 systems engineering, and integration ground support equipment); McDonnell Douglas Corporation (third stage of Saturn 5); Bendix Corporation (guidance components for instrument unit); International Business Machines (instrument unit); General Motors Corporation (guidance and navigation); and ILC Industries (space suits).

List of Illustrations

Log of Manned Flight from Earth to Moon

234,100 miles in 70 hours, 37 minutes, 45 seconds

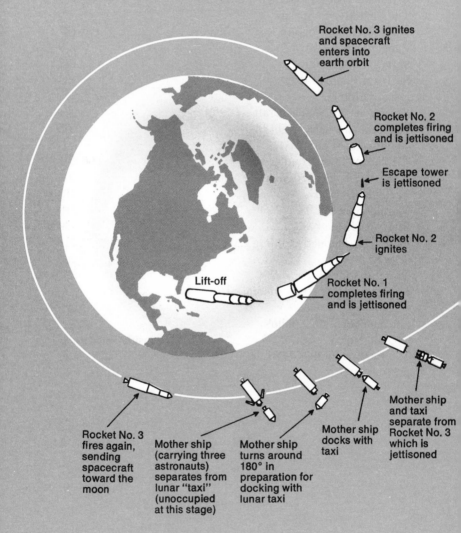

Rocket No. 3 ignites and spacecraft enters into earth orbit

Rocket No. 2 completes firing and is jettisoned

Escape tower is jettisoned

Rocket No. 2 ignites

Lift-off

Rocket No. 1 completes firing and is jettisoned

Rocket No. 3 fires again, sending spacecraft toward the moon

Mother ship (carrying three astronauts) separates from lunar "taxi" (unoccupied at this stage)

Mother ship turns around 180° in preparation for docking with lunar taxi

Mother ship docks with taxi

Mother ship and taxi separate from Rocket No. 3 which is jettisoned

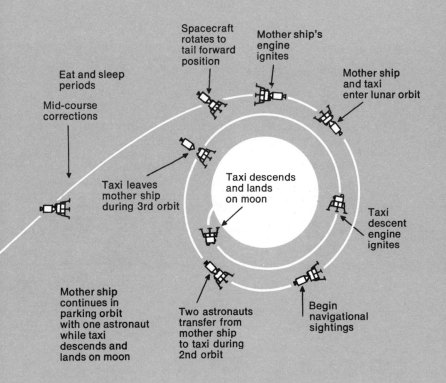

Eat and sleep periods

Mid-course corrections

Spacecraft rotates to tail forward position

Mother ship's engine ignites

Mother ship and taxi enter lunar orbit

Taxi leaves mother ship during 3rd orbit

Taxi descends and lands on moon

Taxi descent engine ignites

Mother ship continues in parking orbit with one astronaut while taxi descends and lands on moon

Two astronauts transfer from mother ship to taxi during 2nd orbit

Begin navigational sightings

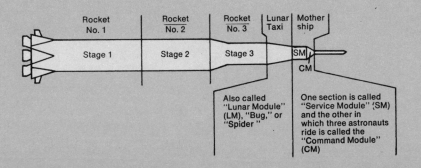

Rocket No. 1	Rocket No. 2	Rocket No. 3	Lunar Taxi	Mother ship
Stage 1	Stage 2	Stage 3		SM / CM

Also called "Lunar Module" (LM), "Bug," or "Spider"

One section is called "Service Module" (SM) and the other in which three astronauts ride is called the "Command Module" (CM)

Log of Manned Flight from Moon to Earth

237,000 miles in 95 hours, 22 minutes, 12 seconds

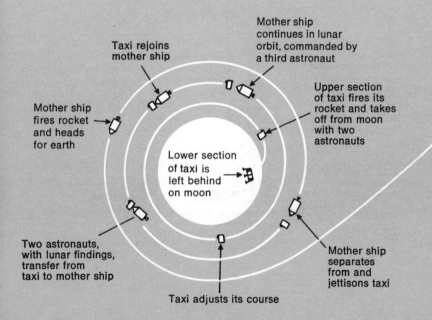

Taxi rejoins
mother ship

Mother ship
continues in lunar
orbit, commanded by
a third astronaut

Mother ship
fires rocket
and heads
for earth

Upper section
of taxi fires its
rocket and takes
off from moon
with two
astronauts

Lower section
of taxi is
left behind
on moon

Two astronauts,
with lunar findings,
transfer from
taxi to mother ship

Mother ship
separates
from and
jettisons taxi

Taxi adjusts its course

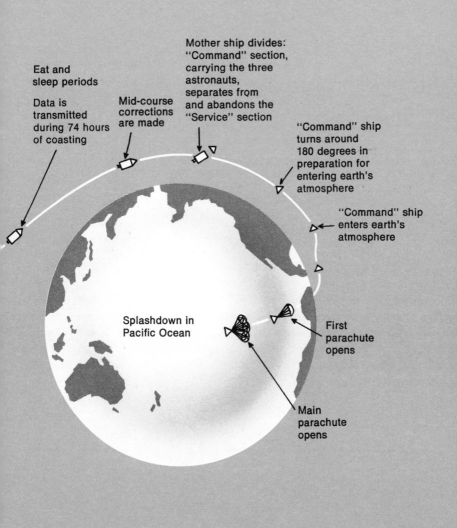

Eat and
sleep periods

Data is
transmitted
during 74 hours
of coasting

Mid-course
corrections
are made

Mother ship divides:
"Command" section,
carrying the three
astronauts, separates from
and abandons the
"Service" section

"Command" ship
turns around
180 degrees in
preparation for
entering earth's
atmosphere

"Command" ship
enters earth's
atmosphere

Splashdown in
Pacific Ocean

First parachute
opens

Main
parachute
opens

Introduction

Many Americans are asking:

Why spend $24 billion to get a handful of rocks from the moon? Though we may be the wealthiest nation on earth, can we afford to go on throwing large sums into space at a time when Negroes are rioting, cities are burning, violence and crime are rampant, schools are in turmoil, pockets of poverty are visible, the air and the rivers are polluted, roads and airports are congested, and the war in Vietnam consumes more and more men and resources?

So go the questions that provide fuel for the case against the U.S. moon and space programs.

Countless speeches, statements, conferences, books, and articles have sought to supply answers and explanations. Yet, on the eve of man's first landing on the moon, public opinion polls indicated that about half the population of the United States still disapproved of the project.

There undoubtedly are many reasons for this disapproval. One of the most important is the difficulty of keeping in mind the basic purpose of our moon mission. This has been obscured partly by history (many already have forgotten the circumstances which produced the Apollo program) and partly by press and television treatment of the space race as something in the nature of a sports contest in the sky.

At the very outset, then, this book recalls the fear which filled the noncommunist world when the Soviet Union suddenly emerged as the number one power in space. It explains the central purpose and meaning of our expedition to the moon in terms of the political, military, and strategic factors which lie at the heart of the space race.

Subsequent chapters provide a simplified explanation of the basic laws of physics, essential for an understanding of how we can get off the ground and into space; a step-by-step account of a trip to the moon and back; a detailed outline of the U.S.–Soviet competition; and a look at the extraordinary panorama of the future, now appearing on the horizon.

These, together with other chapters, should help provide a clearer understanding of our presence in space and of our landing on the moon—perhaps the greatest single feat to date in the history of man.

CHAPTER ONE

Why Go to the Moon?

It all began with a "beep-beep" coming from space. The Soviet government announced that the eerie sound, picked up by radios all around the world, was being sent by an object circling the globe high in the sky. It was christened Sputnik, meaning "fellow traveler"—the first man-made satellite.

The date was October 4, 1957—a day that may be taken to mark the birth of the space age. Soon afterward, scientists were saying that Sputnik's launching represented the most momentous event since the explosion of the first atomic bomb by the United States in 1945.

What made this reedy little beep-beep so momentous? It was not the sound itself, of course, and not just the metal sphere, weighing 184 pounds, from which the sounds kept coming. The significance was, rather, that the Soviet Union had developed sufficient rocket power to lift that much weight to the height and speed required to orbit the earth. This weight was far greater than any that the United States was then planning to put into orbit.

The significance was immediately explained to the public by scientists, military experts, political leaders, and writers in all parts of the world. The underlying meaning, they said, was that the Soviet Union was able to deliver a great package of nuclear destruction to every part of the United States and that this could be accomplished from rocket-launching bases deep inside the Asian heartland.

Adding weight to the threat implied by the satellite were two other important announcements from Moscow—one before and one right after Sputnik—which left little doubt in most people's minds about the frightening significance of Russia's new military power.

Before Sputnik, on August 26, the Soviet Union said that it had successfully tested "a super-long-distance intercontinental multistage ballistic missile" which flew at an "unprecedented altitude." This was estimated at 815 miles, with a speed of 13,700 miles per hour and a range of 5,000 miles.

The Russian announcement added: "The results obtained show that it is possible to direct missiles into any part of the world. The solution of the problem of designing intercontinental ballistic missiles will make it possible to reach remote areas without resorting to a strategic air force, which at the present time is vulnerable to up-to-date means of antiaircraft defense."

This was Moscow's way of saying that the U.S. nuclear-armed strategic air force had been outmoded by Russia's intercontinental ballistic missiles, to which the United States and all other countries were now vulnerable.

The Soviet test had not been witnessed by outside observers, so the claim, at this point, was completely unsubstantiated. However, the beep-beep from Sputnik on October 4 provided all the proof most Western experts needed.

A few days after the Sputnik launching, on October 7, came the second announcement. The Soviet Union said that it had successfully tested a "mighty hydrogen warhead of a new design."

The message was now perfectly clear: The Soviet Union was boasting that it had become the number one military power on earth, having demonstrated the ability to utilize space to deliver weapons of mass destruction to any part of the world. The political meaning also was clear: Henceforth, when the

A replica of Sputnik 1, the first man-made satellite of the earth, on display in Moscow.

Soviet Union spoke, the rest of the world might be expected to sit up and listen with greater regard than in the past, when U.S. strength had overbalanced that of the Soviet Union.

Doubts about the effectiveness of any U.S. deterrent were underscored by the fact that the Soviet successes came at about the same period when the United States suffered two failures in tests of its first intercontinental ballistic missile, the Atlas.

The Soviet announcements sent shudders through the greater part of the world.

Arthur C. Clarke, a well-known British space expert, said: "As of Saturday [October 4] the United States became a second-rate power."

Dr. Theodor Heuss, President of West Germany, sought to calm his people with an appeal not to succumb to "a wave of hysteria."

A spokesman in Egypt said that the Soviet satellite "will make countries think twice before tying themselves to the imperialist policy of the United States."

During a tour of Asia in 1956, Richard Nixon, then Vice-President, warned neutral nations of a "fearful risk" in "friendly neutrality" toward Moscow and Peking. Speaking in Manila, he said that the United States had no sympathy for the "brand of neutralism that makes no moral distinction between the communist world and the free world." After Sputnik, however, there was greater reluctance to draw the "moral distinction" of which Mr. Nixon spoke.

The United States was perhaps more deeply shaken by the Soviet announcements than any other country.

Senator Richard Russell of Georgia, Chairman of the Armed Services Committee, said: "Sputnik confronts America with a new and terrifying military danger and a disastrous blow to our prestige."

Senator Henry M. Jackson of Washington, a member of the Armed Services Committee, described Sputnik as "a devastating blow to the U.S. scientific, industrial, and technological prestige in the world."

Dr. Wernher von Braun—who had played an important role in developing the V-2 for Germany and now was a leading figure in U.S. rocket technology—said that Soviet progress in space was "frightening."

Dr. Joseph Kaplan, Chairman of the U.S. program for the International Geophysical Year, called Sputnik's 184-pound weight "fantastic." It was "fantastic" in comparison with the 21½ pounds that the United States had hoped to orbit.

Within the United States, there was much national self-criticism.

Dr. Israel M. Levitt, Director of the Fels Planetarium in Philadelphia, said that the Soviet triumph was a result of "incredible stupidity" on the part of the United States.

Senator George A. Smathers of Florida, then a member of the Finance Committee, demanded a Senate investigation of the "failure" of the U.S. satellite, rocket, and missile programs.

One of the important reasons for the failure, according to leading educators, was that the United States had seriously neglected the teaching of science and technology.

The annual convention of the American Council on Education, held in Washington, D.C., a week after Sputnik, provided a platform for a general call to the American people to "wake up." The Russians were credited with being alert to the importance of training scientists while Americans "have been complacent too long."

Dr. Franklin D. Murphy, Chancellor of the University of Kansas, said: "We still consider education a luxury rather than a necessity. The little satellite says that our schools are no longer a luxury but are as important as the food we eat. . . . The message it provides is that nothing is more important than a trained and educated mind. . . . We cannot continue to treat education as a second-rate enterprise."

The U.S. Office of Education, reporting results of a two-year study, said that the Soviet Union was outstripping the United States in emphasis on technical and scientific education. It said the Soviet high school graduate, at the end of 10 years, was better educated than the U.S. graduate after 12 years.

Marion B. Folsom, then Secretary of Health, Education, and Welfare, said the report demonstrated "the need to reexamine our whole program of teaching." He added: "We are not giving anything like as much mathematics and science as we should."

Dr. John R. Dunning, a leading U.S. atomic scientist, called for a "drastic new outlook" by Americans and expressed the opinion that the Soviet system "has been able to produce scientists and engineers in certainly greater numbers and quite possibly of higher technical proficiency than our own."

Jean Fabiani, in the French newspaper *Paris-Presse,* suggested that Russia had been able to make such tremendous progress because its totalitarian system enabled it to marshal forces by means not available to the West.

Soviet propaganda, beamed by Moscow Radio to all parts of the world in all languages, played heavily on the theme that Sputnik had proved the superiority of Soviet communism over American capitalism.

Such strong ideas were bound to produce reaction in the United States.

Responding to the complaint of the educators, President Eisenhower on November 13, 1957, called for "a system of nationwide testing of high school students; a system of incentives for high-aptitude students to pursue scientific or professional studies; a program to stimulate good-quality teaching of mathematics and science; provision of more laboratory facilities. . . ."

The core of worldwide concern, however, was in the area of military security. What the noncommunist world waited anxiously to hear from Washington was whether the United States could act swiftly enough to repair the situation.

General Thomas D. White, then U.S. Air Force Chief of Staff, went on record as saying: "Today, in my opinion, air power is the key to survival. In the near future the key will be both air power and space power."

In other words, the noncommunist world could still rely on U.S. long-range bombers and intermediate-range missiles to hold Russia at bay until America could develop the rocket power needed to counteract what the Soviet Union had acquired.

Whether we liked it or not, we were now involved in a space race—not because we sought or desired such a race, but simply because if we refrained from entering it, the Soviet Union would inevitably extend its sway over a greater part of the world. Of that there was little doubt in the minds of serious men in the United States, Europe, Latin America, the Middle East, Asia, and Africa.

The United States hurriedly sought to take up the Soviet

Richard M. Nixon, then Vice-President, holds the instrument package of Explorer 1, the first U.S. earth satellite. With him are Dr. Lee DuBridge, then President of the California Institute of Technology, now President Nixon's science adviser (left), and Dr. William H. Pickering, Director of the Jet Propulsion Laboratory.

challenge. But still more humiliation came on December 6, 1957, when an attempt to launch a beachball-sized satellite with the Vanguard rocket ended in flames on the launch pad at Cape Canaveral (now Cape Kennedy).

In an effort to regain lost prestige, the White House finally agreed to give the Army a crack at launching a satellite. It had earlier turned down an Army satellite proposal because President Eisenhower wanted to keep space from being dragged into the international arms race.

The Army team, led by Dr. von Braun, succeeded at last, on January 31, 1958, in orbiting America's first satellite—Explorer 1. The U.S. moonlet weighed only 31 pounds—a tiny infant when compared with Sputnik 1 and even smaller when compared with

Sputnik 2, which weighed 1,120 pounds.

However late and small, Explorer 1 provided a bit of relief to the United States and the rest of the noncommunist world. It meant that the United States had finally entered the space age.

Soon afterward, President Eisenhower's Science Advisory Committee proposed a broad program of space exploration, including unmanned earth-orbiting observatories, unmanned probes to the moon and nearby planets, and finally manned flights to the moon.

On July 29, 1958, President Eisenhower signed a bill he had received from Congress setting up a National Aeronautics and Space Administration (NASA) as a civilian agency that would direct the advance into space.

NASA put together a bold 10-year plan, proposing a manned space station, manned flights around the moon in the late 1960s, and landings on the moon by astronauts in the 1970s.

Work had already been started on development of a manned satellite called Mercury.

But Congress, upset by the bold Soviet strides in space,

Yuri Gagarin, first man to orbit the earth.

wanted more. The House Science and Astronautics Committee called for a manned expedition to the moon before 1970.

"NASA's 10-year program is a good program as far as it goes," the committee said, "but it does not go far enough.

"A high-priority program should be undertaken to place a manned expedition on the moon in this decade. A firm plan with this goal in view should be drawn up and submitted to Congress."

Then, on April 12, 1961, the Soviet Union again astounded the world, this time announcing that it had placed a man in orbit around the earth for the first time in history. The flight of Yuri Gagarin in a 5-ton spacecraft called Vostok, meaning East, demonstrated that the Russians not only were developing the rocket power for lifting greater weights into orbit than the United States could launch, but had been able to perfect a vehicle that could take a human being into space and return him safely to earth.

Vostok was the most important development in space since Sputnik 1. It came at a time when the United States was work-

Vostok, the first manned spacecraft, returns to earth, landing on the ground (unlike subsequent U.S. spacecraft which land in the water).

ing hard to perfect the Mercury spacecraft to take the first
American aloft. It again demonstrated the superiority of the
Soviet Union in space, and it touched off another wave of
apprehension throughout the noncommunist world.

John F. Kennedy had taken over as the thirty-fifth President
of the United States only three months earlier, and space had
now become one of his major preoccupations. During his
political campaign, he had blamed the Republican Administration for a "missile gap." He soon discovered that the gap was
not in number of missiles, but in rocket power—the brute force
needed to launch large payloads.

Endeavoring to calm the public, the President said: "I do not
regard the first man in space as a sign of the weakening of the
free world." But he warned: "The news will be worse before it's
better, and it will be some time before we catch up."

Words, however, were not enough to dispel the deepening
concern at home and abroad. The situation demanded some
dramatic demonstration of action by the United States.

On May 5, almost on the heels of Gagarin, Commander Alan
B. Shepard, Jr., was boosted to an altitude of 116 miles and
became America's first man in space. But the speed of his
Mercury capsule—5,180 miles per hour—was not nearly enough
to put him into orbit. The flight, though warmly welcomed,
was inadequate for the kind of demonstration that was needed.

President Kennedy instructed his top advisers to examine the
recommendations made by the President's Science Advisory
Committee, Congress, NASA, and the National Academy of
Sciences, and then to suggest a program of action which would
enable the United States to close the gap and restore its position
as technological leader of the world.

It would have to be a program that would stimulate men
of science and industry by providing them with a specific target
on which to focus while developing the skills and equipment
required for overtaking Russia's lead in space. It would also have
to demonstrate dramatically that the United States had achieved
this goal.

One possibility was to undertake a manned flight around the

President Kennedy announces the historic decision to land an American on the moon "before this decade is out."

moon, but NASA expressed fear that there was not enough time to defeat the Soviet Union in this enterprise. Top space officials, however, thought that the United States could beat the Russians to something even more dramatic—landing the first man on the moon. This seemed to meet the need and to offer the best promise of success.

The Soviet Union did not then possess rockets sufficiently powerful to put a man on the moon. For this purpose Russia would have to build new and bigger ones. The United States and the Soviet Union, then, would both be starting from the same point—a new beginning—and the United States would have a good chance to win. The Soviet lead in rocket power would be overtaken and surpassed. The noncommunist world would be able to breathe easier.

On May 25, 1961, in his second State of the Union address, President Kennedy announced the decision to go to the moon

in these words: "I believe that this nation should commit itself
to achieving the goal, before this decade is out, of landing a man
on the moon and returning him safely to the earth.

"No single space project in this period will be more impressive to mankind, or more important for the long-range exploration of space; and none will be so difficult or expensive to
accomplish."

That, in effect, was the decision to proceed with Project
Apollo—developed from a recommendation originally made by
the House Science and Astronautics Committee.

The purpose of the moon mission was both political and
military, and President Kennedy made this clear when he said:

"If we are to win the battle that is now going on around the
world between freedom and tyranny, the dramatic achievements
in space which occurred in recent weeks should have made clear
to us all, as did Sputnik in 1957, the impact of this adventure
on the minds of men everywhere, who are attempting to make a
determination of which road they should take."

According to Theodore C. Sorenson, then a White House aide,
"the President was more convinced than any of his advisers that
a second-rate, second-place space effort was inconsistent with
this country's security, with its role as world leader, and with the
New Frontier spirit of discovery."

Although original estimates indicated that the total cost of
the project might be as high as $40 billion, Congress raised
hardly any questions, notwithstanding the heavy financial bur-
den of new programs to deal with disturbing domestic problems.
Initial funds were appropriated swiftly to send Project Apollo
on its way.

Other reasons, of course, have been given to support this
extraordinary undertaking. Man has been wondering about the
moon perhaps from the moment he first saw it. The idea of
reaching and exploring it has excited his imagination for
ages.

The curiosity of the scientist and philosopher is as great as that
of the explorer and the writer. Man has been engaged in an
endless search for the origin of the earth and thus of himself.

Scientists believe the moon may hold some of the answers.

One famous scientist, holding his thumb and forefinger slightly apart, has said: "Give me a piece of the moon just this big and I will tell you the history of the solar system."

Experts in all parts of the world are anxiously awaiting an opportunity to examine such a sliver.

It is believed, for example, that the composition of a lunar fragment might verify a widely held theory that the entire universe is the result of a "big bang"—an explosion that occurred billions of years ago, involving a sort of "primordial egg" and spraying all of the countless galaxies through space. There are differing views on whether the "big bang" theory could fit a belief in the creation of the universe at the command of a supreme being.

However important these and other factors may be, they do not bear directly on the current urgency in reaching the moon. In the normal course of events, man undoubtedly would have been led by curiosity and a sense of adventure to land on the moon. That would have been in the distant future.

The landing is taking place in our time because a nation no longer can be secure on earth unless it holds a strong position in space. The most powerful instruments of war today are missiles which fly through space. One of our greatest challenges right now is to develop a system for intercepting those missiles. Some of our most important sources of military intelligence are located in space—satellites which can keep an eye on movements by unfriendly, aggressive countries.

Furthermore, space may contain unknown elements which, should they fall first into the hands of an unfriendly nation, could imperil our security and that of the noncommunist world.

The landing on the moon, therefore, was decided upon not primarily for collecting some intriguing samples of lunar soil, but basically for two very different reasons:

First, to provide American scientists and industrialists with a specific objective in space upon which to focus their energies and with a timetable that would oblige them to work at a forced pace.

Second, to provide dramatic proof to the world that the United States had mastered the art of living and working in space, and thereby achieved parity with or superiority over the Soviet Union in this new realm.

This proof might be expected to have a beneficial effect by deterring our foes from embarking on reckless adventures and by assuring our friends that their security, too, has been enhanced by restoration of a better balance of power in the world.

CHAPTER TWO

How We Get There

Flying to the moon may appear similar, in principle, to flying to Istanbul or to any other point on earth. This seeming similarity causes some confusion.

Actually, the airplane and the spacecraft live in two different worlds, governed by different conditions. The airplane must have air to stay aloft. It cannot travel in space because there is no cushion of air to support it.

To get to the moon it was necessary to create a machine that does not depend on air. The rocket was the answer.

Powerful rockets can boost a spaceship through the atmosphere and beyond most of earth's gravity. Once there, the spaceship can coast to the moon with the momentum it has received from its rockets.

There is nothing in outer space to slow its speed or to change its direction.

That's the basic formula for getting to the moon.

However, before scientists could design a moon rocket and the other devices needed for men to eat, breathe, and navigate in space, they had to uncover the basic laws that govern the earth, the moon, and the universe as a whole.

The steps on our road to the moon began in the 1500s with

the discovery that the earth was not the center of the universe—that is, a stationary object with heavenly bodies moving around it. An astronomer in Poland, Nicholas Copernicus, developed the idea that the sun is the center of our system and that the earth and other planets move in orbits around it.

This revolutionary concept began to change man's outlook toward the rest of the universe. It was the beginning of what later became an awareness that a trip to the moon was not just a matter of aiming directly at it and firing. From this start came the realization that it would be necessary to take into account the motions of the two bodies in order to be able to transfer from one to the other. However, Copernicus left many unanswered questions.

About 50 years later, some of these were answered by Johannes Kepler, a German mathematician. He observed that the orbits of the planets and of their moons were not circular but elliptical. He believed that these orbits were governed by natural laws.

However, the character of these laws was not clear to him. Why did the earth and the planets revolve around the sun? Why did the moon revolve around the earth? And what was the magic force that held them in place?

Kepler's ideas led Sir Isaac Newton to develop the laws which established the science of physics. These laws, in turn, provided many of the keys which opened the way for man to lift himself off the earth, rise into space, and reach for the moon and the planets.

Newton's three great laws said:
1. All bodies attract each other in proportion to their size and distance apart *(gravity)*.
2. Every action has an equal and opposite reaction *(thrust)*.
3. An object in motion or at rest will continue that way unless disturbed *(inertia)*.

It is gravity, then, which holds the moon in orbit around the earth, and the earth and other planets in orbit around the sun. Gravity holds all the bodies of the universe in place. It also holds man on the earth.

The Pull of Gravity

The farther from the earth, the weaker the pull of gravity.

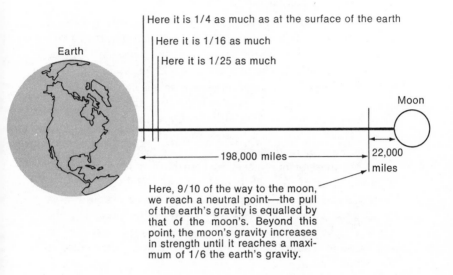

Here it is 1/4 as much as at the surface of the earth

Here it is 1/16 as much

Here it is 1/25 as much

Earth

Moon

198,000 miles

22,000 miles

Here, 9/10 of the way to the moon, we reach a neutral point—the pull of the earth's gravity is equalled by that of the moon's. Beyond this point, the moon's gravity increases in strength until it reaches a maximum of 1/6 the earth's gravity.

To get off the earth, man must break away from gravity's pull by developing a force stronger than this pull. He found such a force in the form of the rocket, which can produce enough thrust to do the job. Once man is in space, Newton's law of inertia permits him and his moonship to coast along at sensational speeds without added thrust.

Gravity is such a familiar phenomenon that we tend to take it for granted, thinking we understand it. For example, people used to believe that objects of different weights fell at different speeds. Not so. Galileo discovered that all objects, regardless of weight, would drop a given distance in the same amount of time, if air resistance or other friction were eliminated.

The earth's constant pull is measured by the rate at which an object accelerates when falling. This rate of increase in speed is always the same—32 feet per second for each second of fall—and measures the pull of gravity that must be overcome to leave the earth. Our rocket must produce a force of acceleration greater than the force at which gravity's tug—in this case deceleration—is holding it back.

The farther away from earth the spacecraft moves, the less it is held back by gravity. Gravity's effect is strongest at the earth's surface and falls off with increasing rapidity as the distance from earth grows. It is very weak at 4,000 miles.

Besides the pull of gravity, the spacecraft is held back in the early part of its journey by the air blanketing the earth. Atmosphere becomes thinner with altitude. Once the rocket rises to about 100 miles, the atmosphere is so thin that it has much less effect on movement through it.

We use most of our rocket fuel in the first few minutes of flight in our effort to reach the orbital speed of 18,000 miles an hour. A rocket burns thousands of tons every second. Still more fuel is used later to accelerate to 25,000 miles per hour, the speed at which the spaceship can escape earth's gravity. At that speed we could travel from New York to San Francisco in about eight minutes.

The task of escaping from the moon, once we have reached it, is easier. Because the moon is so much smaller than the earth, it has less gravitational pull. Also, there is no atmosphere to hold us back. Only about one-sixth the effort is needed to escape from the moon as from the earth. This means that we can use a much smaller rocket carrying only a fraction of the fuel required to leave the earth.

When we return from the moon, the blanket of atmosphere around the earth is helpful in slowing down the spacecraft as it approaches home. Plans for sending a man to the moon would not be practical today if we had to brake by rocket power alone upon returning to earth.

When a spacecraft is in orbit or heading for the moon, the men inside it experience weightlessness. On the surface of the earth, it is gravitational attraction which gives us weight and a sense of which way is down. When a spacecraft is in orbit, gravitational pull downward is balanced by centrifugal force outward. Here, weightlessness is similar to the brief floating sensation you get at the top of a roller coaster. On the way to the moon, weightlessness results from the near-absence of the force of gravity because of the distance from earth.

When we speak here of space, we are using the word in a sense different from the one it usually has on earth. We are referring to the vast distances beyond the earth's atmosphere, where there is almost a total vacuum.

Where does atmosphere end and space begin? There is no simple answer, because atmosphere has no definite boundary. It just continues to thin out into a near vacuum. For every 3 miles of altitude, atmospheric density is approximately halved.

Men can live and work at altitudes from 3 to 5 miles. After that, we have difficulties with our breathing, and are approaching the airlessness of outer space.

On the other hand, at 100 miles up, there still is too much atmosphere to permit a satellite to orbit permanently. Beyond that distance, interference by the atmosphere becomes less and less. For practical purposes, then, 100 miles is considered the beginning of space.

Newton's second law—that every action has an equal and opposite reaction—is the basis of rocket power. How does it work?

How the Rocket Works

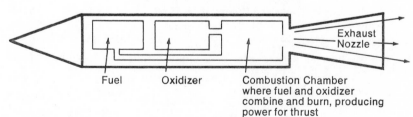

Fuel   Oxidizer   Combustion Chamber
where fuel and oxidizer
combine and burn, producing
power for thrust

Pressure is equal on all 4 sides of combustion chamber until valve is opened for exhaust

Gas then pushes through the nozzle. Pressure on the forward side pushes the rocket upward

Reaction is felt when you fire a gun. The recoil of the gun into your shoulder is the reaction. Most of the time, we notice only the action, but the reaction always occurs. Without it, motion is impossible.

This reaction, in a rocket, is called thrust. Thrust is also what happens when you turn on your garden hose and the reaction to the force of the water shooting outward makes the hose try to move backward in your hand.

In the same way, when gas escapes from the nozzle of a rocket, the reaction pushes the rocket in the opposite direction. We get thrust by burning fuel in a space called a combustion chamber. The gas pushes equally on all the walls of the chamber, but escapes through a nozzle at the bottom of the rocket. As the gas escapes, a force equal to the downward push is applied to the forward end of the chamber and the rocket rises. This reaction to the escaping gas is thrust. The amount of thrust depends on how much hot gas is escaping and how fast it moves out the nozzle. The greater the thrust the more weight you can lift off the ground, and the farther you can go in space.

Scientists cannot tell us *why* these natural laws work the way they do. They can only tell us *how* they do it.

The Chinese used the principle of thrust in rockets at least as early as the thirteenth century. The rocket used in fireworks displays is familiar to all of us and operates, basically, the same way as moon rockets.

The Chinese sealed a hollow tube at one end and filled it with gunpowder. They held the gunpowder in with a light paper plug and passed a fuse through the plug. They fastened a stick to the tube and stuck it in the ground so that the closed end of the tube pointed up. When they lit the fuse, it ignited the gunpowder, which burned and produced a great deal of gas. The pressure of the expanding gas pushed out the plug, and the gas rushed out the opening. The thrust or reaction to the escaping gas against the opposite wall of the closed tube pushed the rocket into the air.

This reaction is not connected with the air around the tube. In fact, air only slows the progress of the rocket. A rocket is most

How Thrust Works

Reaction to the force of water shooting outward
pushes the hose backward in the fireman's hands.

efficient in space, where there is no air to hold it back.

To make a rocket lift off, we must provide more thrust than
weight at the launch site, or the rocket will not move. As the
rocket accelerates, the weight of its fuel is reduced, so it accelerates more and more rapidly until it reaches the speed at
which it can orbit—nearly 18,000 miles per hour—or escape
gravity—25,000 miles per hour.

Sending a rocket to the moon might be compared with throw-
ing a stone over a house. If you don't throw the stone hard
enough, it won't go over the peak of the roof. It will fall short,
pulled down by earth's gravity. To overcome gravity long
enough to get the stone over the roof, you must give the stone
enough speed to do the job. So it is with getting a rocket to
overcome gravity. It must have enough thrust to perform its task.

Why 25,000 miles per hour? Galileo told us that all upward-
moving objects will have their speed decelerated by gravity 32
feet per second. If a rocket were launched, for example, and
its engines were shut down when it reached a speed of 100 feet
per second, gravity would subtract 32 feet per second from its

speed at the end of one second. At the end of two seconds, it loses another 32 feet, and still another 32 at the end of a third second. By this time, its speed is only 4 feet per second, and that is very quickly lost to gravity. After only 4 seconds, then, it begins to be pulled back to earth.

Mathematical calculations tell us that a spaceship must reach 25,000 miles per hour—7 miles per second—in order to get far enough away to escape gravity temporarily and coast to the moon.

To make a spacecraft orbit the earth is a different proposition, involving a combination of gravity and inertia.

Imagine a cannon on a platform 100 miles above the earth, where the atmosphere is so thin that the drag of air resistance is slight. If you fire a cannonball parallel to the earth's surface at a speed of 18,000 miles per hour, it will fall 16 feet in the first second as a result of the pull of gravity. (It reaches a rate of 32 feet per second only at the end of one second, so it falls only 16 feet during that first second.) In that same second it will also have traveled 5 miles. It so happens that the curvature of the earth drops 16 feet every 5 miles. As a result, the path of the cannonball parallels the curvature of the earth, and the cannonball, maintaining its speed because of inertia, will be able to keep orbiting indefinitely.

A spacecraft does the same thing. If it wants to break the orbit and return to earth, it simply reduces its speed and is pulled down by the force of gravity. If it wants to head for the moon, it simply increases its speed, breaks out of orbit, and moves farther away from earth and its gravitational pull.

Why does a spaceship going to the moon first orbit the earth? It could travel directly to the moon, but several orbits of the earth give the astronauts time to be sure that all equipment is working properly and to make any necessary adjustments before continuing the trip.

It takes great quantities of fuel to produce the rocket thrust to get off the earth. Engineers, therefore, are using gravity and inertia in moving spacecraft between the earth and the moon. For example, they supply just enough thrust to raise the space-

Orbiting the Earth

When a cannonball (or a spacecraft) reaches a speed of 18,000 miles per hour, it is traveling fast enough to resist being pulled down to earth, but not fast enough to escape the influence of gravity. It therefore moves in orbit around the earth.

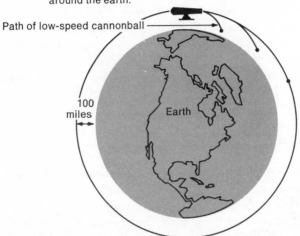

Path of low-speed cannonball

100 miles

Earth

craft outward into space, beyond the strong grip of earth's gravity. The ship now has enough momentum to be able, without further rocket thrust, to coast through the vacuum to the moon. When it gets close enough to the moon, the ship comes under the moon's gravitational pull and falls toward it. By approaching at the proper angle and then reducing speed, the spacecraft can drop into orbit around the moon, following the same principles governing the orbit of the earth.

For the return trip the spacecraft, with a short burst of rocket power, can break out of lunar orbit, coast with the benefit of inertia toward the earth, and then allow itself to fall to earth, pulled, as by a powerful magnet, by gravity.

In this way ships in space utilize the forces of inertia and gravity much as ships at sea once used the currents and winds to propel themselves.

However, it took many years after Newton proclaimed his laws before man learned to apply them to travel in space. The interval between discovery of the laws of physics and development of the engineering techniques for applying them was filled with perceptive pieces of science fiction.

For example, Jules Verne, a Frenchman writing in the nineteenth century, 100 years before Project Apollo, described a manned flight to the moon which was extraordinarily prophetic.

In his book *From Earth to the Moon,* three men and two dogs were fired from the mouth of a gigantic cannon sunk in the Florida soil just across the peninsula from the Cape Kennedy launch site. They rode a 10-ton missile around the moon and back to earth and were rescued from the Pacific Ocean by a ship. His description showed great respect for scientific fact. He calculated carefully the energy required to fly away from earth.

Verne did not have his explorers land on the moon. He knew that the moon was desolate and uninhabited. Since he could figure no believable way to fire his travelers back from the moon's surface, he had them circle the moon and swing back.

Today, Apollo flights are launched on the same kind of path followed by Verne's "astronauts." Verne even used small rockets to steer his vehicle in space. At the time, he did not realize that rockets could be made powerful enough to do the whole launching job.

Perhaps the most prophetic thing about Verne's tale was his assertion that Americans would inevitably be the first men to fly to the moon because "the Yankees . . . are engineers—just as Italians are musicians and Germans are metaphysicians—by right of birth."

In spite of Verne's prophecy, Americans made no serious effort to develop rocket power until a century later. Earlier steps were taken in other countries.

The first to show that rockets could be used to push away from the earth was Konstantin Tsiolkovsky, a Russian. Half a century ago he studied the possibility of rocket-powered flight to the moon. He understood the importance of speed in order to escape gravity. He recognized that the first problem in going to the moon was to secure a high exhaust speed from the rocket and build a strong rocket structure.

After his hero "applied the lighted match," Jules Verne's rocket of a century ago, bearing extraordinary resemblance to our Apollo spacecraft, takes off for the moon, as shown in this illustration from the French writer's book.

However, Tsiolkovsky's work was not taken very seriously at the time.

Another early pioneer who was ridiculed by many of his contemporaries was an American, Dr. Robert Goddard. Working in the United States early in the twentieth century, he built and tested a number of rockets, including the first to exceed the speed of sound. More than anyone else, he developed rocketry into a science which examined and tested theories of propulsion and flight characteristics on which subsequent research was based.

One of the important areas Goddard studied was that of liquid fuels. Solid fuels—refinements of the gunpowder used long ago by the Chinese—did not have the thrust for moon travel. They were also unstable and often did not burn evenly so that the rocket veered off course. Liquids were more powerful and it was possible to control their rate of flow and burn.

By the time Goddard refined the liquid fuels, the components of a rocket engine were fairly well established. They are the fuel tank, oxidizer tank, fuel pump, oxidizer pump, pump motor, and combustion chamber.

The fuel, which is most often kerosene, and the oxidizer, usually pure oxygen, make up the propellant. The fuel is what burns; the oxidizer is what helps the fuel to burn. They are stored in separate tanks and are pumped as needed into the combustion chamber. In our Saturn 5 moon rocket, the motor which runs a fuel pump is more powerful than the motors which run our largest ocean liners.

The fuel and oxidizer ignite in the combustion chamber, and the hot gas rushes from the nozzle to give the rocket thrust.

The early engineering efforts of Tsiolkovsky and Goddard were not supported by the great sums of money and the manpower necessary to develop a workable moon rocket. They simply were not popularly regarded as worthwhile. Development lagged until World War II, when the Germans saw the potential of the rocket as a weapon. The cost of making a new and superior weapon was justifiable in the course of war, so development of the rocket was given high priority.

Dr. Robert Goddard and his liquid-propellant rocket, just before its first flight, at Auburn, Mass., March 16, 1926.

Hitler Germany's V-2, the "father" of present-day missiles and rockets.

German engineers converted the rocket from a curiosity into the V-2 missile. It could carry a 1-ton warhead 200 miles at more than 2,500 miles per hour. More than 4,000 V-2s were launched by the Germans in 1944 and 1945. General Dwight D. Eisenhower said that if the V-2 had been developed six months earlier, "our invasion of Europe would have proved exceedingly difficult, perhaps impossible."

The V-2 was such an advance that many people refused to believe it existed. It set new records in speed, range, altitude, and power. It was the first man-made object to reach space, rising almost 100 miles above the earth. One version was conceived for a trans-Atlantic attack on New York City.

After World War II, von Braun, who had been in charge of the German rocket development program, came to the United States with more than 100 of his top men. Even after that, development in the United States was slow until we realized how near the Soviets were to being able to go to the moon.

Working for the Army, von Braun and his team developed the missile which put the first U.S. satellite into orbit three months after Sputnik. They formed the nucleus of a much larger team which designed and built the Saturn 5 rocket—a direct descendent of the V-2 missile. The V-2, for its part, used much of the technology and engineering developed by Goddard.

Improvements in rocket design after the flights of the V-2 were not changes in concept. Engines were made more efficient, and fuels were developed which produced more energy.

One notable advance was the multistage design. This calls for several rockets, each with its own fuel tanks and its own engine, stacked on top of one another. Presently, the practical limit of the stack is three, the first one lifting all the others as well as itself. In this arrangement, the main or booster rocket is first. It reaches its maximum altitude and speed, then drops off the bottom of the stack. This procedure is repeated with each stage, so the vehicle does not have to carry for the total trip all the empty fuel tanks. It is more practical than developing one huge rocket to do the entire job and carry all its empty weight along.

This principle has been applied with great success to Saturn 5, which generates the thrust needed for lifting three astronauts off the earth and sending them on to a landing on the moon.

Once the rockets and fuels had been developed to provide the basic thrust and propulsion, countless other feats of engineering were required to enable the astronauts to maneuver in space, to maintain constant communication by radio with the earth, to breathe, and to perform physical functions in an unnatural environment. A way also had to be found to bring the men through the atmosphere on their return to earth without their being destroyed by the fire of friction.

All told, the system carrying the men to the moon and back involved more than 6 million separate parts, representing the efforts of 400,000 men and women.

Furthermore, the equipment had to be virtually perfect. With a reliability of only 99.9 percent, statistically it would still have more than 6,000 failures. This means that the equipment had to be designed for a reliability of 99.999 percent or better.

Engineers of today who produce and operate such equipment and the great men of yesterday who discovered the basic laws of physics are the heroes of the saga of man's flight to the moon.

CHAPTER THREE

Our Lunar Base

Although the race to the moon was triggered by the cold war, scientists have long wished it were possible to go there for good reasons of their own.

Strange as it seems, they are mainly interested in the moon because, compared with the earth, the moon has remained virtually unchanged over billions of years.

Now, with the landing of astronauts, we have a chance to study the early history of the solar system and perhaps of the universe. Men walking on the moon are stepping billions of years into the past.

Most scientists believe that the moon could never have supported any form of life as we know it or that, if life did begin there, it must have perished early. For one thing, all life on the earth requires both air and water. The moon has no atmosphere, and there are no traces of free water on its surface.

If the moon once did produce the ingredients for an atmosphere, these would have been lost because the moon's gravity is too weak to keep oxygen, nitrogen, and the other gases that give life to earth from escaping into space. And without an atmosphere, there could be no water on the surface.

As scientists see it, the main reason for believing that the moon has always been devoid of air, water, and life is its size. It has a diameter of 2,160 miles, compared with the earth's nearly 8,000. From our planet, scientists have been able to determine that the moon is made up of material not nearly so dense as the earth's rocky outer crust and core of molten metal. Scientists estimate that the moon weighs only one eighty-secondth as much as the earth.

Fortunately for us on earth, our atmosphere serves as a blanket and a filter. The extremes of heat and dangerous radiation that stream from the sun are filtered, and only a fraction reaches our planet. At night, the atmosphere retains heat, keeping the thermometer from plunging far below zero.

The moon is not so fortunate. Devoid of an atmospheric filter and blanket, the moon's temperature soars to more than 250 degrees in daytime and drops to about 280 degrees below zero at night. A single step from sunlight to shadow would take a person from oven heat to the cold of instant freezing.

Just as radiation from the sun beats directly on the moon, meteorites crash into its surface unimpeded, causing many of the craters visible on its surface. Meteorites hit the earth, too, but most are burned and destroyed by the friction of the atmosphere before they can reach the surface.

The moon's smallness gives it other characteristics unlike anything man has ever experienced before. It has mountains towering as high as 27,000 feet, but they are easily lost from view. The moon's small size makes its curvature more pronounced than the curvature of the earth. An observer several miles away from the moon's mountains might not see them because they would be over the horizon.

The same phenomenon makes it possible to stand at the bottom of a large lunar crater and still be unable to see the rim.

In the absense of atmosphere, we cannot speak to one another on the moon as we do on the earth. Our astronauts must communicate by radio or by making signs.

The lack of atmosphere also makes it impossible to have long-range radio communication between distant points on the moon. On the earth we can bounce radio signals off the upper

The Moon—Physical Facts

Diameter	2,160 miles (about ¼ that of earth)
Circumference	6,790 miles (about ¼ that of earth)
Distance from earth	238,857 miles (mean; 221,463 minimum to 252,710 maximum)
Surface temperature	250 (sun at zenith) −280 (night)
Surface gravity	1/6 that of earth
Mass	1/100 that of earth
Volume	1/50 that of earth
Lunar day and night	14 earth days each
Mean velocity in orbit	2,287 miles per hour
Escape velocity	1.48 miles per second
Month (period of rotation around earth)	27 days, 7 hours, 43 minutes

atmosphere and transmit them to the other side of the world. On the moon, radio transmissions are limited to very short ranges.

With gravity on the moon only one-sixth as strong as it is on earth, a home-run hitter in a lunar baseball game could drive a ball well over half a mile. A golfer's drive from the tee would sail clear over the horizon.

To earthlings adjusted to the stronger pull of gravity back home, this curious moon characteristic has both advantages and disadvantages.

It makes it necessary to plan every physical move with care, but at the same time it gives man the effect of being 6 times stronger because he weighs 6 times less than on earth.

Other characteristics of the moon are strikingly different from anything we have known before.

The lunar days and nights, by our standards, are each 2 weeks long. This is due to the moon's very slow rotation on its axis. While the earth makes a full rotation every 24 hours, it takes the moon almost 4 weeks to make a complete turn.

By a quirk of nature, the moon, traveling at 2,300 miles per hour in its orbit around the earth, circles our planet in about the same period that it turns on its axis. For this reason, we never see the moon's back side from earth.

The rotational period and the orbital period are not exactly matched, however, and the moon has a slight wobble in its path around the earth. We always see the same face of the moon—41 percent of its surface. Another 41 percent we never see. This leaves some 18 percent of the moon's surface alternately visible and invisible.

On the moon, there is no sound, no smell, never a raindrop, never a breeze. There is no spring, summer, or fall; nothing to break the monotony—just an endless succession of silent, motionless days and nights, each utterly alien and hostile to human life.

Viewing the skies from the moon's surface, one might conclude that all the universe is just as barren. The stars are in view night and day, but they never twinkle because there is no disturbed atmosphere which makes them appear to do so. The vast millions of miles of space between stars are pitch black.

From the moon the sun appears to be a ball of intolerably bright radiance, but the sky around it is as black as midnight.

The view of the earth from the moon is breathtaking. Hanging like a giant, agate marble against the blackness, it dominates the sky. Just as we see the moon slowly change phases, observers out there will see the earth grow from a slender crescent into a glorious disk so bright that it gives the moon an eerie twilight at night.

What do scientists expect to learn in an empty place like the moon?

First, they hope that the moon, because it is essentially changeless, will give them sharp new insights into the history of the earth and the solar system. The material the moon is made of may provide clues to the basic manner in which all the universe was built.

Many scientists believe that the earth and the moon and the rest of the solar system were formed at the same time from an enormous cloud of gas swirling through space. Over billions of succeeding years, it is believed, the gas may have begun to become more dense as the particles attracted one another. Eventually, then, solid bodies would have formed and the solar system would have emerged. The entire universe may have formed essentially this way.

Bodies large enough to start nuclear chain reactions and begin burning became stars like our sun, which is now in its middle age. Intermediate-sized bodies became planets, and the smaller ones moons.

Certainly our moon is not unique as a natural satellite. Mars has 2 moons, Jupiter 12, Saturn 10, Uranus 5, and Neptune 2. Our moon is unusual, however, because it is much nearer the size of the planet it accompanies than is any other moon in the solar system.

An old, old theory holds that our moon was once a part of the earth itself. When the planet was new, it was thought, it was still a semimolten ball, spinning so rapidly that a day lasted no more than two or three hours. Gradually, the planet spun itself into the shape of a pear or a light bulb, and the stem

The first close-up photograph of the crater Copernicus, showing mountains in the foreground rising to a height of 1,000 feet and a peak in the Carpathian Mountains on the horizon rising to a height of 3,000 feet. The distance from the horizon to the

se of the photograph is about 150 miles. The horizontal distance across the part the crater seen here is about 17 miles. The photograph was taken by Lunar biter 2 when it was 28 miles above the surface of the moon.

popped off, falling into space and thus forming the moon.

Another view is that the moon formed in another part of the solar system or even outside it, that it was an asteroid or an independent planet which passed so near the earth that it was captured in the earth's gravitational field.

Theories about the formation of the moon have come and gone as long as man has studied the heavens. Manned exploration of the moon is making it possible to substitute facts for theory about the moon and the earth.

Scientists now believe the earth is about 4.5 billion years old. They calculate this in an ingenious way.

The radioactive element uranium, in an extremely slow-acting process, loses its radioactivity and becomes lead. Pure uranium, after 2.25 billion years, will become 25 percent lead.

There are uranium-bearing rocks scattered all over the world. By measuring comparative amounts of uranium and lead in these rocks, it is possible to calculate how old they are. In this way, scientists have put the age of some rocks they have uncovered at more than 3.6 billion years.

But it has been possible to go even deeper into history. By the same technique, some meteorites that have fallen on the earth from space have been estimated to be 4.5 billion years old.

If the solar system did form at once, and these meteors came from within our own solar system, then it can be supposed that the earth is at least that old, too.

Some objects which have come down to the earth from space may even come from the moon. It is believed that small, glassy bodies called Tektites may have been splashed into space by meteorite impacts on the moon, and that they drifted until they were captured by the earth's gravity.

The earth has changed too much, and it is changing too rapidly, for scientists ever really to trace its earliest years. The difference between the ages of meteors and the oldest rocks uncovered on earth suggests that there is a period of at least a billion years missing from our knowledge of the earth.

It is difficult to appreciate how fast the earth does change, but oceans, rivers, winds, volcanoes, earthquakes, and glaciers, in addition to the activities of man, reshape the face of the earth. Mountains can appear and disappear in 100 million years.

This seems almost forever, but it is a fairly short time in geological terms. The reshaping of continents, the rise and fall of mountain ranges, the movement of glaciers all bury the records of the earth's history.

But because the moon is changing so slowly, the early history of the solar system should be still intact there.

If the moon is the same age as the earth, scientists estimate that the original material from which it formed should be no more than 50 feet beneath the surface. In some areas where there is no sign of meteorite impacts or volcanic activity, the material could still be on the surface, bleached by 4.5 billion years' exposure to the sun.

Scientists want to find whether these rocks are like the ancient ones they have studied on earth. They can tell whether the rocks were formed by volcanic activity or whether they have been unchanged since the beginning of time. In this way they will eventually be able to tell with great assurance whether the moon and the earth have the same early history, whether the solar system formed as they think it did, or whether the moon came from somewhere else and happened to be trapped by the earth's gravity.

While geologists want the moon to settle ancient questions about the formation of the earth and the solar system, they also want to understand how the moon's features were created.

Many of the 30,000 craters were produced when large meteorites fell from space, hitting the surface at thousands of miles per hour. When this happens, the energy of dozens of hydrogen bomb explosions is released; rocks and boulders are thrown for miles; small debris is hurled into space with such speed that it escapes the moon's gravity and continues drifting through space.

The meteorites themselves punch deep into the moon's crust, releasing such heat that rocks melt and molten material erupts from beneath the surface and flows in streams away from the crater. The tell-tale sign in most craters formed in this violent way are peaks in the center of crater floors, pushed up by shock waves rebounding from the impact.

It is conceivable that even some of the moon's smooth, dark areas, mistakenly called "seas," were formed in this way. Spaceships flying over the moon are tugged downward in their orbits when they pass over some of the seas, indicating that massive objects, perhaps huge iron meteorites, are buried beneath the floors. They exert enough gravitational pull to make space vehicles flying 60 miles above deviate from their orbits each time they pass over.

If a meteorite big enough to produce these circular seas on the moon hit the earth, it would devastate an area larger than the state of Texas.

Such objects do hit the earth occasionally. Small ones have even injured people. Fortunately, most meteors burn in the atmosphere on the way through. These are the shooting stars we sometimes see at night.

In studying meteorite craters on the moon, scientists have long used as a model a gigantic crater in Arizona that looks exactly like many of the impact craters on the moon. Believed to be 30,000 years old, it is several hundred feet deep and more than a mile wide. The object which caused the crater is believed to have weighed 15,000 tons or more. So much energy was released when it hit that the meteorite exploded into millions of pieces.

Since astronomers began studying the moon with telescopes as early as the seventeenth century, why haven't they seen one of these cataclysmic events take place?

Again, it is necessary to sharpen our perspective on geological time.

To create the 30,000 craters discernible from earth on the near side of the moon in 4.5 billion years, it would require no more than one impact every 1,500 years. We should not wonder that we have not seen one of these huge craters formed. The moon is indeed changing slowly.

It has become apparent that forces other than meteorite impacts are at work changing the face of the moon. There are geological features bearing unmistakable evidence of volcanoes.

The surface is sprinkled with low, dome-shaped structures identical to those associated with volcanic activity on earth. There are other classic volcanic features such as cone-shaped mountains with craters in their peaks.

We know now that some of the smaller craters once believed to have been caused by meteorites probably have volcanic origins.

When unmanned probes began to photograph the moon up close, scientists found millions of small craters, down to inches in size, which had been beyond the view of even the most powerful telescopes on earth. Some of them apparently were caused by tiny meteorites. Others resulted from falling debris from eruptions.

Though there is abundant evidence of volcanic activity, we still cannot say with certainty that it is going on now. If a volcano erupted on the moon, it seems reasonable that we would detect it from earth. But we must ask the same question we asked about impact craters, and we come to the same conclusion: It is probable that we have not been watching the moon long enough.

There are other forces at work, but of less importance. Tremors sent through the crust from meteorite impacts upset boulders and rocks resting precariously on the walls of other craters, sending them tumbling to the bottom.

Gravity, weak though it is, causes landslides, sending material slipping down into valleys and craters.

All this is happening so slowly that even 4.5 billion years have not too substantially changed the moon from the way it was in the beginning.

Man's desire to get to this desolate place and explore it increased as he came to appreciate fully the enormous size of the universe.

It sometimes seems that we are going too far away as we seek to establish a foothold on the moon. But, in relation to the universe, the moon is in our back yard. It presents man with a unique opportunity to explore beyond the confines of his own planet and to find whether he is really capable of flights into deeper space.

Where once we thought the earth was at the center of all creation, we now know the earth is one of the smaller planets around a thoroughly undistinguished star in an average galaxy, the Milky Way. This middle-class galaxy has 100 billion stars and stretches across an area hundreds of thousands of light years in diameter. (A light year is the distance light travels in a year at a speed of 186,284 miles per second.)

Scientists are now certain that there are 100 million or so galaxies like our own within 2 billion light years of us, and that they are formed into clusters. These clusters are the largest known systems of organized matter.

The smallest known system, on the other hand, is the atom, the basic building block of everything from a grain of sand to these clusters of galaxies rotating through space. It would take 250 million atoms lined up side by side to cover an inch. An atom is like a miniature solar system, with electrons circling the nucleus as planets go around the sun. The atom, like our solar system and the universe, is mostly empty space.

In most of man's previous exploration, he has found it more difficult to find and reach his new frontiers than to establish himself once he was there. It will be different on the moon because it is so far away, so hostile.

Exploring new worlds before, men have usually been able to find some new resources in usable form wherever they went. Often they have been able to establish permanent outposts on their first expedition. But on the moon there is nothing readily usable. The men who visit it carry along every ounce of food, water, and fuel to get back home, even the air they breathe.

If this were not difficult enough, the exploration of the moon is further restricted because at present only two men can go to it at a time with equipment developed for Project Apollo. Moreover, they are limited to a stay of a few hours on the surface.

Is it possible, then, for man ever to stay on the moon for longer periods of time?

The crater Langrenus, about 15 miles in diameter, as photographed by
Apollo 8 during the first manned flight around the moon. The spacecraft
was about 150 nautical miles above the crater when it took this picture.

Indeed it is. For years, engineers have been working on designs of moon stations and vehicles to carry men miles to explore and collect scientific samples.

Geologists want to leave the smooth equatorial landing sites to study the inside of meteor craters, volcanic areas, and the polar zones. They want to drill into the surface at many different points and set off small explosions to help find what kind of structure is deep beneath the surface and whether the moon has a molten core.

Getting sufficiently established on the moon to do extensive exploration and research will be as difficult as getting there in the first place.

In the initial years of moon exploration, landing vehicles will serve as shelters, scientific laboratories, living quarters, and radio stations. In far years ahead, visitors to the moon will work in underground stations covered over by the moon's surface material to shield them from heat and cold.

Provided an atmospheric cocoon, the inhabitants of these stations will be able to live in comfort, moving in air-pressurized tunnels through an underground network of laboratories. Dressed in pressurized space suits, they will go above ground for excursions of days or weeks into the lunar badlands.

The stations may well be international colonies, much like scientific stations in the Antarctic.

First, man will have to find more economic ways of getting to the moon with both passengers and the huge loads of cargo necessary to construct permanent outposts.

The exploration for usable natural resources in the moon's crust will begin early. Perhaps these will be gold or diamonds, but moon explorers will be far happier if they find water or substances they can use for rocket fuel.

Water is needed not only for drinking, but for cooling electrical equipment, for heating and air conditioning, and for growing food. The electrical generating devices called fuel cells used in manned space vehicles produce some water. They generate electricity through a chemical reaction between hydrogen and oxygen, and water is a by-product.

Permanent moon stations will probably require nuclear power plants because they can generate large amounts of electricity over long periods with a very small amount of uranium or plutonium fuel.

It is possible that there is water on the moon. If, for example, the moon was once a part of the earth, it could have taken a huge amount of water with it when it was spun away. If it passed very near the earth and was captured, its gravity could have siphoned water away from the earth's oceans. Today the moon's gravity, weak as it is, is still strong enough to pull the earth's seas and oceans, thereby causing our tides.

Some scientists believe that there is a layer of ice—like permafrost in the Arctic—not far beneath the moon's surface, insulated well enough that it does not melt under the searing midday sun. Others have suggested that there is boiling water deep within the moon, and that even today steam is escaping through lunar fissures. This suggests the possibility of steam-powered, steam-heated and cooled moon colonies.

Or it may be possible to extract water from the moon's rocks. Scientists have detected evidence of sulfur at some places on the moon's surface. On earth, sulfur is invariably associated with water-bearing rocks. But to extract water from the rock itself will require enormous sources of energy.

Bizarre schemes have been suggested. One idea is to place huge, metal-foil mirrors at places in space called "libration points," where the gravity of the earth and the gravity of the moon are balanced. Theoretically, objects placed at these points would remain there, drifting neither toward the earth nor toward the moon. Giant mirrors so located would require only tiny control jets to keep them oriented so they could concentrate and focus the sunlight on a desired point on the moon. That would drive the temperature as high as 800 degrees, enough to chemically break down the rocks, making it possible to capture their water.

Growing food on the moon is an especially interesting problem. What we call moon soil may be extremely poor or void of plant nutrients, but we might turn to a science called "hydroponics" to produce vegetables.

Years ago, scientists found they could grow plants without soil. The technique involves using tanks filled with chemically-treated water. Wire mesh screens are placed over the surface of the water and covered with rocks or cinders. Such materials merely hold the plants in place; the roots stick down into the water and grow there. Some plants flourish this way, producing more and better fruit than they do growing in rich soil.

This technique was used to produce green vegetables for U.S. forces on some arid Pacific islands in World War II, and it has made great advances since then. The weak gravity on the moon might even make it possible for hydroponic plants to grow faster than they do on earth. Experiments in satellites have shown that weightlessness affects some plants in strange ways, making them grow in different patterns and grow faster than they do in their natural environment.

Until ways are found to develop resources on the moon, explorers will have to make more and more efficient use of what they have. Even human waste materials will have to be carefully saved. Some of it, urine for example, will be treated to extract fresh drinking water.

The successful search for sources of oxygen or hydrogen would be as important as the discovery of usable water on the moon. This would raise the possibility of one day refueling rockets on the moon for their return trip to earth, or even for missions deeper into the solar system.

It is the nature of rocket vehicles that most of their weight and volume is taken up with fuel. On trips to the moon they must carry along enough fuel to get them back to earth. If ways could be developed to refuel on the moon, it would be possible to substitute useful payload for some of the fuel which has to be launched from earth.

As we look ahead to the time when man will establish himself as a resident of the moon, we might ask about the moon's potential for military uses. Can operations on the surface of the moon do anything to enhance our national security back on earth?

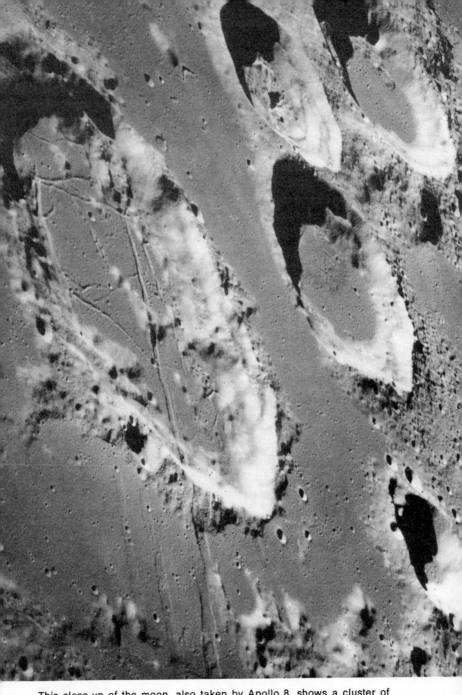

This close-up of the moon, also taken by Apollo 8, shows a cluster of craters. The largest, Goclenius, is 40 miles in diameter.

In the early days of the space age, there were real fears that the Soviet Union's lead would enable the Russians to establish control of the moon. When any potential adversary can operate in an environment where we cannot, it is a matter of great concern to military planners.

Now, an international treaty, signed by both the United States and the Soviet Union, forbids placing weapons in space or on the moon. It also prohibits a country from making territorial claims on the moon.

From a technical viewpoint, it would be possible to establish missile launching pads on the moon to send bombs against targets on earth. The best insurance we have against this happening is the moon's great distance from us. If an intercontinental missile were fired at the United States from the Soviet Union, we might have no more than 15 minutes' warning, because the approaching warhead is shielded from radar detection by the horizon until it is in the latter phase of its flight.

On the other hand, a missile launched from the moon to the earth could probably be detected two or three days before arrival, giving time for defensive missiles to be launched to intercept it in space.

By the same token, it offers no advantage to use the moon for spying on earth when this can be done infinitely better by satellites in low earth orbit. Looking at the earth from the moon one cannot see evidence that our planet is inhabited. But satellites in earth orbit can even spot missile sites and detect rocket firings.

Satellites can be placed in stationary orbits so they observe the same point on the earth's surface all the time. At an altitude of some 23,300 miles, such satellites travel around the earth in the same time it takes the earth to turn on its axis; the result is that the satellite stays in the same place in relation to landmarks on earth.

Such constant surveillance can never be possible on the moon, even if some magical devices could be built which would allow observation of small objects. A given area on the earth would be in view only half the time because of the earth's rotation.

Nevertheless, weapons on the moon could have blackmail potential just as a nuclear power could intimidate other nations by placing a bomb in earth orbit. It might be psychologically intimidating.

As for nonmilitary aspects, scientists have planned an exhaustive search for any evidence of life. They would be most surprised if they found any, but the possibility cannot be altogether discounted. If there is not life in the form of viruses or bacteria, there might conceivably be molecules left over from the process of life formation on earth. As we shall see in a later chapter, elaborate precautions have been taken to insure that moon explorers do not bring back and release some germs that we would be powerless to combat.

If the possibility of finding some crude form of life on the moon is farfetched, the idea of using the moon as the site for exciting new astronomical laboratories is not.

Just as the atmosphere filters out most of the radiation sent our way by the sun, it forms an opaque window which lets us see only a little of the energy coming from the stars. So, despite the advances of modern astronomy, scientists still have to do a great deal of guesswork about the characteristics of stars and their life and death.

In recent years, some of the most exciting discoveries of science have come from the field of radio astronomy. Gigantic telescopes which collect radio energy are making it possible to study the universe in an entirely new way.

But radio telescopes miles in diameter are needed to really take advantage of the opportunity to study the noise from the stars. It is difficult to find sites for such laboratories because of their susceptibility to interference from electronic equipment on earth.

The back side of the moon is an ideal place. Protected from all interference, a radio telescope could gather information unobtainable either on earth or in earth orbit. Here again, the low gravity on the moon would offer an advantage. It would be possible to put up a gigantic receiver like a child's erector set. The structure could be built without the massive support required on earth, where gravity would make it topple.

In recent years, astronomers have discovered objects called quasars which seem to be so far away that their radiation we are now receiving was emitted before the solar system was formed. Even now they appear to be moving away from us at velocities approaching the speed of light.

Radio energy is being studied from other objects called pulsars, which seem to be extremely small, yet generate incredible amounts of energy. They send out pulses so accurately timed that when they were first discovered it seemed that they might be intricate radio signals from another civilization somewhere.

Our lunar base, then, will extend our vision and hearing so we may perceive a greater part of the universe than has ever before been apparent. At the same time, it will enable us to look back closer than ever toward the day of creation.

CHAPTER FOUR

Space-Age 'Hardware'

The easiest way to understand the difficulty of sending men to the moon is to examine the "hardware" required to make the trip possible. From the giant Saturn 5 rocket to the smallest of the 3.5 million parts making up the Apollo spacecraft, this machinery represents the summit of engineering and manufacturing capability in the mid-twentieth century.

When historians look back at the race for the moon, they will probably study it in relation to world politics, the Cold War, or the costs and results of the project. They probably will not dwell on nuts and bolts. Who, for example, knows the details of Columbus's ships or Charles Lindbergh's *Spirit of St. Louis?*

However, today it is still possible to appreciate the extraordinary technical achievement of building the machinery for flights to the moon. The task demanded a whole new way of looking at engineering problems.

First, Apollo was designed to operate in an airless, weightless environment—and do it with greater reliability than anything ever built before. In addition, it was designed with extreme restrictions on weight.

Weight limitation was the first problem to consider, because it affected the design of every part of the vehicle. Because there is a limit on the size of the rockets men can build and launch, the Apollo spacecraft had to be squeezed into a package weighing no more than 50 tons, including fuel. This required developing lightweight materials and miniature electronics beyond anything engineers had even considered before.

New paints and insulation were developed to save weight on the rocket itself. Seats were eliminated from the design of the moon vehicle. Delicate computers and navigation equipment were built, with many vital components too small for the naked eye to see. Even the weight of drugs in the astronauts' medical kits was considered.

Into the 12-foot tall Apollo command capsule, engineers wove enough electrical wiring for 50 two-bedroom homes. The Saturn 5 rocket contains 2.5 million soldered electrical connections. Engineers have calculated that, if each connection had one extra drop of solder and one thirty-second of an inch of unnecessary wire, the excess would weigh more than the rocket's payload, the Apollo spacecraft.

The moon landing vehicle was built with the smaller stresses of lunar gravity in mind. Workers on earth could not even stand in its cabin to install instruments because they would mash the floor out of shape. A device similar to a diving board was extended into the cabin so that men could lie on it while working inside.

The stairs on the landing vehicle were designed for use only on the moon. If a man climbed them on earth, they would bend double under weight 6 times that on the moon.

This gives a general picture of what made the design and manufacture of the Apollo system so radically different from any task American industry had attempted before. Now let us examine the requirements of each component.

First, the Saturn 5 rocket unquestionably is the most powerful machine ever developed. Its history illustrates how far in advance such an engineering undertaking must be planned. Development actually began in 1958 on the engines which power the Saturn first stage. Long before the race for the

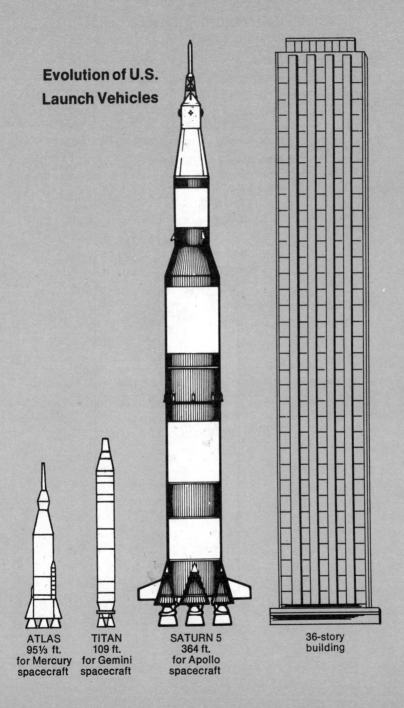

Evolution of U.S. Launch Vehicles

ATLAS
95⅓ ft.
for Mercury
spacecraft

TITAN
109 ft.
for Gemini
spacecraft

SATURN 5
364 ft.
for Apollo
spacecraft

36-story
building

Apollo Spacecraft/Saturn 5 Rocket

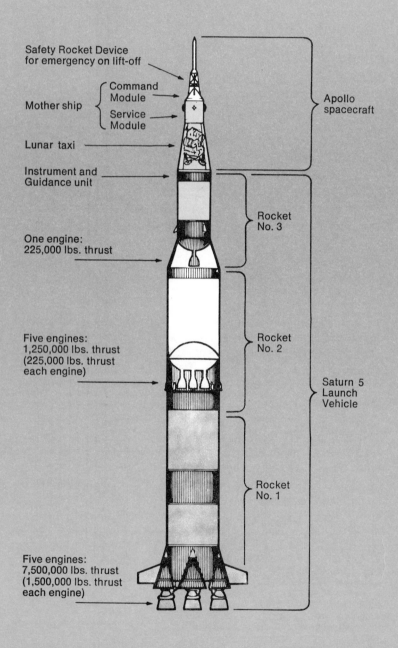

Safety Rocket Device for emergency on lift-off

Mother ship
- Command Module
- Service Module

Lunar taxi

Instrument and Guidance unit

One engine: 225,000 lbs. thrust

Five engines: 1,250,000 lbs. thrust (225,000 lbs. thrust each engine)

Five engines: 7,500,000 lbs. thrust (1,500,000 lbs. thrust each engine)

Apollo spacecraft

Rocket No. 3

Rocket No. 2

Rocket No. 1

Saturn 5 Launch Vehicle

moon began, or planners realized how big a booster the United States would need, it was decided to start developing a rocket engine which would produce a thrust of 1.5 million pounds. By clustering engines with this capacity, it was then possible to build boosters of truly enormous power.

The basic booster is powered by kerosene. Oxygen is carried along because the booster climbs to altitudes where the air is too thin for combustion unless the rocket brings its own oxidizer. Oxygen is pumped into its five engines along with the fuel to make the kerosene burn.

It was soon recognized that engines burning kerosene with liquid oxygen would not be efficient enough for the upper stages of very large rockets. Rocket designers turned to liquid hydrogen as a fuel because it produces more thrust per pound of weight than kerosene. While kerosene produces about 300 pounds of thrust per pound of fuel burned, liquid hydrogen produces a thrust of about 425 pounds. Engineers decided early that they had to take advantage of this added efficiency to send very heavy payloads into space.

In 1960, the United States started developing a large, hydrogen-burning engine. This engine powers both the second and third stages of the Saturn 5. Five of them are clustered in the second stage, and a single engine pushes the third stage.

The over-all result is an enormously powerful rocket. Von Braun, chief designer of the Saturn 5, has said it could send a Volkswagen all the way out of the solar system.

As mentioned, the Saturn launching system is three different rockets stacked on top of one another. The booster stage lifts the whole stack, plus the Apollo spacecraft, to an altitude of more than 37 miles. This rocket pushes with a thrust of 7.5 million pounds. After that, the second stage takes over with its thrust of 1 million pounds and sends the spacecraft to an altitude of roughly 100 miles. Then the third stage ignites, putting the Apollo into orbit. This last engine develops 250,000 pounds of thrust.

Although liquid-hydrogen fuel has indisputable advantages over other liquid propellants, it is a highly volatile, dangerous fluid unless it is handled with extreme caution. It can even explode on mere contact with certain metals.

Liquid hydrogen must be kept at a temperature of 423 degrees below zero or it begins to boil, turning into gas. Hydrogen is not very dense, so even as a liquid it takes up a lot of space. Saturn's fuel tanks must be of tremendous size to carry the necessary load. Even though the low density of the fuel permits the tanks to be built of thin, lightweight material, it is a major problem to insulate them well enough to keep the hydrogen liquid. While the fuel must remain at –423 degrees, the outside temperature at the Florida launch site may be approaching 90 degrees. Insulation materials in the tanks of Saturn's upper stages keep the hydrogen chilled even though the walls of the tanks are only 1½ inches thick. They are so well insulated that ice cubes placed inside the tanks would take several years to melt.

While liquid oxygen is not as volatile as hydrogen, it also presents difficult problems because it must be maintained at about 297 degrees below zero to remain liquid.

Despite the effective insulation of the Saturn fuel tanks, they must be permitted to vent, or breathe out, almost until the moment the rocket blasts off. Otherwise, the hydrogen and oxygen turning into gas inside them would build up enough pressure to rupture the tanks. To keep the tanks full of liquid fuel, they must be continuously fed more liquid gas until launch is imminent, or the vehicle would start its journey without a full load of fuel.

From bottom to top, Saturn has a total of 41 rocket engines. The 5 kerosene-oxygen burners in its first stage and the 6 hydrogen-oxygen burners in its two upper stages provide all the propulsion.

The remaining 30, some generating as little as 72 pounds of thrust, include both solid- and liquid-fueled engines. Some are fired to settle propellants into the tanks before the main upper-stage engines fire, and others are used to aid the separation of the rocket's stages.

When the first stage shuts off and separates from the second

The first stage of the Saturn 5 rocket. Its five engines produce 7.5 million pounds of thrust to lift the spacecraft off the ground and to launch Apollo toward the moon.

stage, for example, eight forward-pointing solid-fuel rockets fire for half a second. They slow the used-up first stage and keep it from coasting into the second stage and damaging that unit before its engines ignite.

About three years are needed to build each Saturn 5. The first stage is assembled by the Boeing Company at a government plant near New Orleans where tank engines were once manufactured. The second stage is built in California by North American Rockwell Corporation, which also makes the command and service capsules of the Apollo spacecraft. The third stage is manufactured by the McDonnell Douglas Astronautics Company at Huntington Beach, California.

All three rocket stages are test-fired before they arrive at

Cape Kennedy to be stacked into a single vehicle. Because of their enormous size—33 feet in diameter—the first two stages have to be moved by giant barges from the assembly plants to a remote test site in southern Mississippi. The second stage has to travel through the Panama Canal to get from California to the Gulf of Mexico, then to Mississippi through an inland waterway.

In Mississippi, the first two stages are locked into massive concrete and steel stands resembling pyramids and are test-fired. The third stage is tested in the same way in California and is flown to Cape Kennedy in a modified military transport plane called the "pregnant guppy" because of its outsized fuselage.

The three sections making up the Apollo spacecraft are flown to Cape Kennedy from their own assembly plants. The command and service sections come from North American Rockwell, and the lunar landing craft comes from Grumman Aircraft Engineering Corporation at Bethpage, Long Island, New York.

The three rocket stages and the three sections of the Apollo spacecraft finally come together in Kennedy Space Center's Vehicle Assembly Building, which towers more than 50 stories above the Florida countryside. (This building is so large that clouds can form inside it near the roof, producing an indoor rainfall.)

The assembly building is located on Merritt Island across the Banana River from Cape Kennedy proper. Cape Kennedy itself is the launch site for the Air Force's Eastern Test Range (formerly the Atlantic Missile Range). Its facilities are made available for many of NASA's launches.

Until the Boeing Company constructed a new building to assemble its 747 Jumbo Jet, NASA's vehicle assembly building was the world's most spacious structure. It is roomier than the Pentagon, which houses most of the headquarters of the U.S. Department of Defense.

Dozens of cranes and lifting devices mounted at the ceiling and around two tall assembly bays enable engineers to work on

Vehicle Assembly Building, Cape Kennedy, with Apollo/Saturn 5 vehicle at right.

A Saturn 5 rocket, with an Apollo spacecraft nestling on top, is carried from the Vehicle Assembly Building to the launch pad at Cape Kennedy in preparation for a flight to the moon.

the simultaneous stacking of two moon vehicles. The rockets are fitted together on launch platforms the size of baseball diamonds. The platforms are moved into the assembly building on a huge, caterpillar-tracked vehicle called a crawler.

Cranes lift and stack the rocket stages. The moon landing vehicle is mounted on top of the third stage, and on top of that come the command and service sections of Apollo. When the moon rocket is all fitted together, it towers 36 stories above the launch platform.

About two months before the scheduled launch of the rocket, the building's doors—said to be the world's largest—open. The crawler emerges, carrying the rocket in an upright position along with a launch tower which enables workers to move up and down the side of the rocket to work on it as they go through final preparations for launch. It is like seeing a New York City skyscraper picked up and moved.

Each of the four tracks on the crawler is 10 feet high and 40 feet long. It edges along at a speed of less than half a mile per hour, driven by two 5,500-horsepower diesel engines. It carries the Saturn 5 rocket and the Apollo spacecraft to the launch site 3½ miles away, moving along a roadway wider than an eight-lane freeway.

Other engines on the crawler power hydraulic jacks, which keep the platform precisely level as the vehicle creeps along. The whole structure—crawler, rocket, launch tower, and launch platform—weighs more than 17 million pounds. A rock roadbed 7 feet thick is needed to bear the weight.

The launch area, reinforced with steel and concrete, rises 48 feet above sea level. As the crawler climbs this hill to place the rocket for launch, the platform tilts so that the rocket and launch tower are kept perfectly vertical. Once it reaches the site, the crawler leaves its almost unbelievable payload and moves away.

During the next two months, the rocket and spacecraft are given final checkouts and are put through mock launches. The rocket is even fueled in a practice exercise before it is finally ready for flight.

Apollo Spacecraft
Service Module

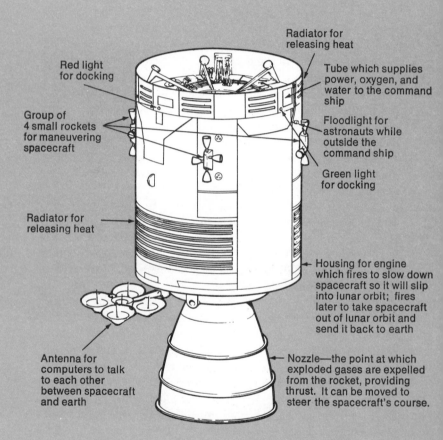

Radiator for releasing heat

Red light for docking

Tube which supplies power, oxygen, and water to the command ship

Group of 4 small rockets for maneuvering spacecraft

Floodlight for astronauts while outside the command ship

Green light for docking

Radiator for releasing heat

Housing for engine which fires to slow down spacecraft so it will slip into lunar orbit; fires later to take spacecraft out of lunar orbit and send it back to earth

Antenna for computers to talk to each other between spacecraft and earth

Nozzle—the point at which exploded gases are expelled from the rocket, providing thrust. It can be moved to steer the spacecraft's course.

The Service Module supplies thrust, electricity, oxygen, and water to astronauts and their command ship.

Prior to development of the assembly and launch concept used for Apollo, multistage rockets were put together at the launch site. They were exposed to the weather for months as they were being prepared for flight. The vehicle assembly building now makes it possible to carry out the final assembly in a carefully controlled environment, free of dirt, dust, and other contaminants and kept at carefully controlled temperatures. If a severe tropical storm is predicted for the area, the crawler can, in a matter of hours, move the whole assembly back into the protection of the building.

Still more impressive than the staggering dimensions of the Florida moonport and the Saturn 5 rocket are the precision and reliability of the Apollo spacecraft itself. Its elaborate computers, flight-control systems, and communications devices for maintaining contact with a worldwide tracking and control network would allow Apollo to operate efficiently even without men aboard.

Manned, the system could stay in space for days or even go to the moon and back without assistance from support crews on earth. The vehicle is almost as far advanced over the Mercury spacecraft which first took American astronauts into space as modern jetliners are over the crude airplanes which the Wright brothers first flew.

The vehicle we call the Apollo spacecraft, as mentioned earlier, is composed of three sections called modules—designed to meet three basic needs.

First is the need for a unit in which Apollo's three astronauts can live and work. This is provided by the command module— the cockpit or brain center of the spaceship. It has to be rugged enough to survive the fiery plunge back into earth's atmosphere on the return trip from the moon.

Next is the need to provide the command module with rocket power for getting into lunar orbit and then out of orbit for return to earth. Electric power and various other things such as water, food, and air for the crew cabin are also required. These are all provided in a barrel-shaped section, with a rocket engine at its base, called the service module.

An Apollo Command Module, being checked out from the manufacturing plant, ready for mounting atop a Saturn 5 rocket for a trip to the moon.

Apollo Spacecraft
Command Module

Where the astronauts live and work

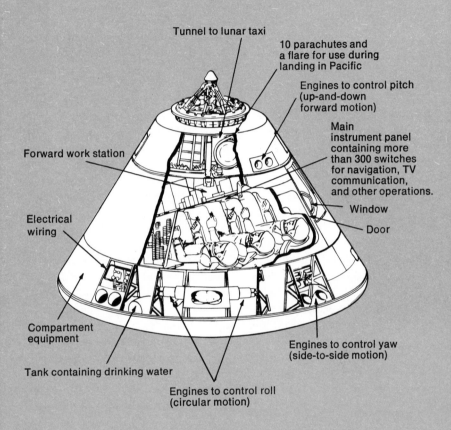

Tunnel to lunar taxi

10 parachutes and a flare for use during landing in Pacific

Engines to control pitch (up-and-down forward motion)

Main instrument panel containing more than 300 switches for navigation, TV communication, and other operations.

Window

Door

Forward work station

Electrical wiring

Compartment equipment

Tank containing drinking water

Engines to control roll (circular motion)

Engines to control yaw (side-to-side motion)

Four clusters of small rockets, mounted on this module's sides, are used to point the spacecraft in the right direction before the main propulsion engine is fired. Also, antennas for communication with earth are attached to the sides of this section.

Finally, there is the need for a separate, smaller spacecraft to descend to and later rise from the moon's surface—a shuttle, or taxi. This is met with the third section, known as the landing module.

The blunt end of the command section is covered by a heat shield that protects the astronauts from high temperatures encountered upon reentering the earth's atmosphere.

Throughout the flight to the moon and back, the command and service sections remain locked together as a single unit. They separate only as they approach earth on their homeward journey, and the service section is discarded in space. The command section turns around so that the heat shield will face forward. The shield is designed to withstand the several-thousand-degree heat resulting from atmospheric friction.

The third part of the Apollo vehicle, the lunar lander, shuttles two men between the command craft and the surface of the moon. This space taxi is one of the most unusual flying machines ever built. It acts like a helicopter, but uses small rocket thrusters to descend and rise in the moon's airlessness.

When the Apollo spacecraft is launched from earth, the lunar landing craft is stored inside a protective cover between the third stage of the Saturn rocket and the service section of Apollo. Its landing legs are folded spiderlike beneath it. It is not activated until Apollo is beyond earth orbit and is on its way to the moon.

Then the protective panels, which guard the lander from damage during launch, are thrown away. The command section hooks up with it out in space where, because of reduced gravitational pull and absense of air blast, there is little risk of damage to its fragile structure.

The lunar lander has to be light enough to get off the moon with limited rocket power. Yet it also has to be strong enough

Lunar Module 'Taxi'

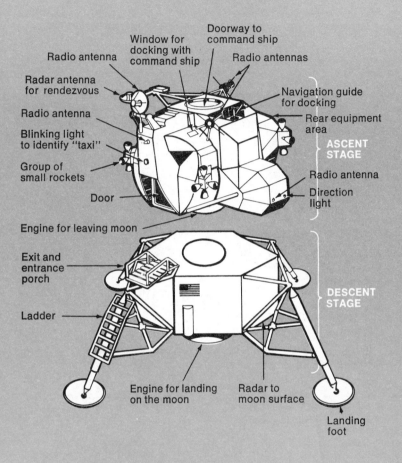

Radio antenna

Window for docking with command ship

Doorway to command ship

Radio antennas

Radar antenna for rendezvous

Navigation guide for docking

Radio antenna

Rear equipment area

Blinking light to identify "taxi"

ASCENT STAGE

Group of small rockets

Radio antenna

Direction light

Door

Engine for leaving moon

Exit and entrance porch

DESCENT STAGE

Ladder

Engine for landing on the moon

Radar to moon surface

Landing foot

The lower part of the moon-landing vehicle
(also called the "Lunar Module" or the "spider")
is left behind by the astronauts.
The upper part is used to take off from the moon
and to return the astronauts to the command ship.

Apollo Spacecraft

POSITION
IN SPACE

Lunar Module
"Taxi"

POSITION
ON LIFT-OFF

Command Module

Service Module

Lunar Module
"Taxi"

to protect the astronauts from the vacuum of space and the blazing sun that heats the moon to more than 250 degrees.

Because there is no way to rescue astronauts stranded on the moon, the lander's take-off engine has to be reliable beyond question. Also, it has to be simple to operate. The astronauts do not have the benefits of the large and complex launch center that initially sent them on their way from Florida.

The lander also has to carry a life-support system to sustain astronauts exploring the moon for several hours and navigation equipment to guide it to a rendezvous with the command ship for return to earth.

When planners debated the scheme for shuttling two men to the surface of the moon from orbit, they considered a number of alternatives.

The simplest approach called for a landing device that was little more than a "flying belt." This would have lowered an astronaut, protected only by a space suit, to the surface of the moon. Another idea was for a lander which would remain on the moon for a very short time.

Space engineers finally settled on what, in comparison, seems a luxury model—a landing vehicle with an elaborate life-support system that permits explorers to take a few hundred pounds of scientific equipment down with them and bring back 50 pounds or more of moon soil and rock samples.

The lunar lander can stay on the moon for 35 hours. With modifications, it could support two astronauts on the surface for a week or more. The craft has two rockets. One, with an engine that can be throttled, is used for landing. The other is used for takeoff. The lander, besides being a spaceship, provides men on the moon with shelter, a scientific laboratory, and a radio-television transmitter.

The astronauts ride in a pressurized compartment nearly 8 feet wide. They stand before a dual instrument panel and windows which are slanted down toward the surface so that they can lean over and see the spacecraft's front footpad when it comes to rest on the moon's surface.

The airtight cockpit is covered by welded aluminum alloy

and by a 3-inch layer of insulating material. Overall is a very thin aluminum-alloy skin.

Although it seems fragile, the lander is sturdy enough to withstand a jarring impact on the moon's surface if the astronauts misjudge their height and shut off their engine too soon. Its life-support system maintains the cabin's temperature at a comfortable 75 degrees, even though, outside, it may be well over 200 degrees. In areas of the craft where the exhaust from the rocket engine might beat against the structure, insulation is designed to protect the men from temperatures of more than 1,800 degrees.

Outside the taxi, astronauts are protected by space suits—costing $100,000 each plus millions of dollars to develop—which keep them cool and comfortable even if they find moving around in them to be physically taxing. They are protected by liquid-cooled underwear and an inflated suit insulated by layers of nylon and teflon, covered with a fireproof material made of glass fiber. The suit also includes a waste-management system. (While in the command ship, solid wastes are collected and sealed in plastic bags for postflight analysis; liquid wastes are dumped overboard.)

Their helmets, which look like the round containers on bubble gum machines, are double-layered to protect them against the sun's radiation and the danger of cracking the helmet in a fall. Inside the helmets are movable, tinted visors which can be shifted in front of the eyes to cut the glare of the sun.

Beneath their space helmets the astronauts wear cloth caps equipped with microphones and earphones to allow them to communicate with each other and with the Houston control center while they are sealed in their moon suits.

Their gloves have thermal insulation which enables them to pick up extremely hot or cold objects without injury. The fingertips are made of silicone rubber so that the explorers still have a sense of touch.

On their backs, the astronauts carry massive packs which send water through a network of small, nylon tubes woven throughout their undergarments. These packs, called portable

Moon Suit

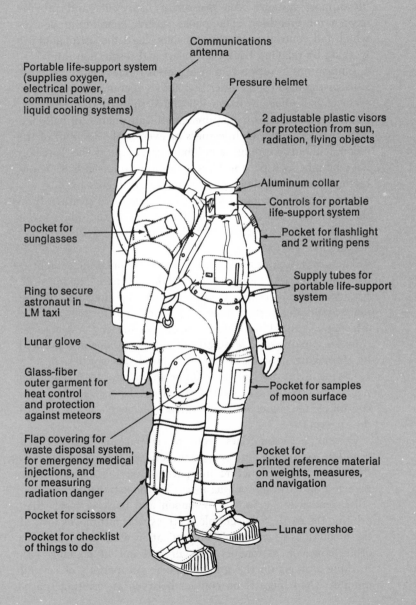

Communications antenna

Portable life-support system (supplies oxygen, electrical power, communications, and liquid cooling systems)

Pressure helmet

2 adjustable plastic visors for protection from sun, radiation, flying objects

Aluminum collar

Controls for portable life-support system

Pocket for sunglasses

Pocket for flashlight and 2 writing pens

Supply tubes for portable life-support system

Ring to secure astronaut in LM taxi

Lunar glove

Glass-fiber outer garment for heat control and protection against meteors

Pocket for samples of moon surface

Flap covering for waste disposal system, for emergency medical injections, and for measuring radiation danger

Pocket for printed reference material on weights, measures, and navigation

Pocket for scissors

Lunar overshoe

Pocket for checklist of things to do

life-support systems, also pressurize their suits and provide oxygen for breathing. The packs include monitoring devices which tell controllers in Houston how hard the astronauts are working by relaying back their heart and respiration rates.

Innovations to support lunar explorers range from such necessities as the moon suits described above to equipment that may seem trivial. Office workers who have suffered from smudgy, erratic ballpoint pens will appreciate the advantages of ballpoint pens that write in weightlessness or even in the vacuum of the moon without skipping, smudging, or failing. (The Russians have bought such pens in large quantities from the U.S. manufacturer for use in their own manned spaceflights.)

The camera developed to send back television pictures from the moon represents a new frontier for this medium because it can take pictures even during the lunar night without using floodlights.

The ground equipment that supports manned spaceflight is as impressive and indispensable as the vehicles that go aloft. Engineers sitting before control consoles in Houston can tell more about the performance of a space vehicle than can the astronauts aboard it. This is made possible by a computer complex capable of making 80 billion calculations per day and by a tracking network stretching around the world.

During every second of a flight to the moon, information pours into the control center. Even as the astronauts sleep. control center engineers keep watch over every system aboard the spacecraft.

Computers, using data from radar tracking stations. can calculate course changes as accurately as can the astronauts themselves. A malfunction in space or on the moon can be detected on earth as soon as it can by the astronauts.

In some ways. flying to the moon and back is easier than orbiting the earth. For example, as the spacecraft moves toward the moon, it is in constant communication with earth. In earth orbit, however. astronauts pass in and out of contact with tracking stations on the ground. There are periods of several minutes when there is no contact between an orbiting spacecraft and the Mission Control Center. To keep in closer touch, ground tracking stations are assisted by tracking ships and instrumented airplanes positioned at critical points along the path of an orbiting spacecraft.

The communications problem does not occur on moon flights because the Apollo spacecraft is always in view of one of three 85-foot tracking dishes, located at Goldstone, California; Honeysuckle Creek, Australia; and Madrid, Spain.

Thirty years ago, the urgent demands of World War II forced advancement of aviation, radar, and other forms of electronics at many times the speed that they would have developed under normal conditions. Now, similarly, entire fields

A giant antenna dish, perched in the mountains near Madrid, Spain, tracks an Apollo spacecraft on a flight to and from the moon.

of science and engineering are being pushed forward at rates and to degrees that ordinarily would have required decades of slow evolution.

The hardware developed for our lunar program is in the forefront of this explosion of new knowledge.

CHAPTER FIVE

Voyage to the Moon

There is a moment of triumphant excitement when preparations for a flight to the moon are completed.

Everything that can be done has been done. In three minutes, three men will be on their way to explore, for the first time, another part of the solar system. Two men will land on the surface of the moon—a quarter of a million miles from home— and face the most hostile frontier man has ever tried to cross.

A control room 3½ miles from the base of the towering Saturn 5 rocket gives the final clearance to blast off, and computers take control of the fantastically complex machine.

With lightning speed, they race through thousands of final checks, from the five huge, bell-shaped engines at the bottom of the rocket to an emergency escape tower 364 feet above the launch pad pointed toward the sky.

The astronauts settle themselves in their couches, eyes sweeping the wall of switches, gauges, and controls before them, and assure the launch director that all is well in the Apollo spacecraft.

Overhead, supersonic jets are waiting to photograph the rocket as it climbs into space. In Houston, Texas, halfway across the country, engineers are ready to assume control of the mission as soon as the booster engines clear the service tower standing beside the rocket on the pad.

Beneath the spacecraft, cavernous fuel tanks holding nearly a million gallons of kerosene, liquid oxygen, and liquid hydrogen are being pressurized. Electrical cables drop away.

Up and down the Florida beaches, hundreds of thousands of Americans listen to the countdown on radios, waiting to see Saturn carry Apollo into space in the most dramatic moment of man's race for the moon. Around the world television screens show the drama as it takes place. The tension and excitement of Cape Kennedy span the earth.

Launch controllers edge forward in their seats as computers tell them that the more than 6 million parts making up the magnificent moon machine are in perfect condition.

The last crisp, confident reports come from the Apollo spacecraft commander, as a public affairs officer says from the control room:

"We just passed the 25-second mark in the count . . . 20 seconds, we are still GO . . . T minus 15, 14, 13, 12, 11, 10, 9. . . . We have ignition sequence, the engines are on." And the countdown continues to zero, then . . . LIFTOFF!

Suddenly, the violence is beyond comprehension. Saturn's giant engines hurl torrents of flame ricocheting hundreds of feet, a blinding orange curtain almost obscuring the rocket itself, as the engines gather their full 7.5 million pounds of thrust, 160 million horsepower. For six seconds, the rocket is held in place, moving not an inch as the hammering flames seemingly threaten to sink Florida into the sea.

Thunder from the mighty booster rolls for miles. Dust sprinkles down from the ceiling in the control room. Buildings tremble. Birds are frightened to flight. Four miles away, observers feel as though their insides were turning to jelly as the shock waves hit.

It's like the eruption of a volcano. Tremors speed through the earth's crust, and time seems to stand still.

Finally, the rocket begins to rise. Consuming more than 3,600 gallons of fuel per second, it pushes itself away from the earth. It is like seeing the Washington Monument take flight. For the first seconds, it seems as if it may falter, slow, and fall back to the launch pad.

Then, 13 seconds after the orange flame erupted, the rocket struggles past the top of the service tower.

"Clear of the tower!" the launch director yells in the control room. It is the signal for engineers in another control room at the Manned Spacecraft Center in Houston to take over.

At last, man is on his way to the moon.

Slowly gathering speed as it rises, the vehicle pitches gently over the Atlantic, its riders feeling themselves pushed into the backs of their couches by increased gravity forces.

The Saturn 5 leaves a milk-white trail as it hits the cold upper atmosphere, a tail of flame stretching hundreds of feet behind. One minute and 17 seconds out, the vehicle goes through a critical period when the rocket is under its severest strain. At an altitude of 38 miles and a speed of 6,000 miles per hour, the booster shuts off as suddenly as it came to life. Then Saturn's second stage starts firing, carrying the astronauts on toward orbit. The spent first stage is detached and plunges back toward the sea.

By now, the pilots are giving Houston confirmation that the first big hurdle is behind them. With a thump, the launch escape rocket, no longer needed, is jettisoned. Now the astronauts have a stark, clear view of the sky, unobscured by earth's atmosphere.

They are still pinned to their couches by the rapid acceleration of the second-stage rocket. But now the ride is silky smooth as they climb toward an altitude of 100 miles.

Florida is far behind them as they head across the Atlantic, their speed reaching more than 15,000 miles per hour. After six minutes, the second-stage rocket is spent like the first.

The third stage takes over and pushes the spacecraft to 18,000 miles per hour, making it now an artificial satellite of the earth.

The astronauts have been gone from Cape Kennedy 11 minutes, and they have reached a plateau where they can

17 Steps
to the Moon

1. Huge crawler carries rocket and spacecraft to launching pad.

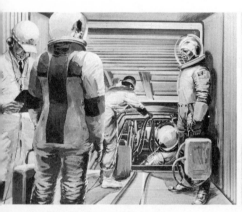

2. Three astronauts enter the command spacecraft.

3. Lift-off: Apollo astronauts leave Cape Kennedy for the moon.

4. After 2½ minutes, first rocket stage falls away and second stage ignites.

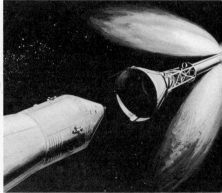

5. Launch escape device, not being needed, is jettisoned.

6. Second stage burns 6½ minutes; third stage goes into earth orbit.

7. After checkout in orbit, third-stage firing sends craft to the moon.

8. Adapter panels open; command/service section pulls away.

9. The command/service section turns and docks with the lunar landing craft.

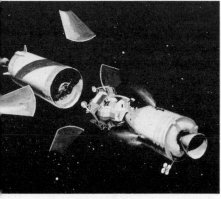

10. After docking, spacecraft separates from the rocket's third stage.

11. The service section fires to slow the spacecraft into lunar orbit.

12. Two astronauts transfer to landing craft to prepare for descent to moon.

13. Landing craft separates from mother ship, leaving one man behind.

14. Landing craft descends to the surface, leaving mother ship in orbit.

15. Landing craft's descent engine fires as taxi comes in for a landing.

16. One astronaut checks taxi while the other waits inside.

17. The two men explore the moon, get samples, and place testing equipmen

prepare to break away from the earth's hold and aim for the moon.

They started their journey with a space vehicle weighing nearly 6.5 million pounds and standing 36 stories tall. Discarding the first two Saturn stages after use, they now have a spaceship 140 feet long, weighing some 300,000 pounds.

This includes the Apollo spacecraft, the third stage of the Saturn launch vehicle, and nestled between them, the vehicle that will take two of the astronauts to the surface of the moon.

Still only about 100 miles above the earth, the explorers start getting adapted to the strange feeling of weightlessness. Instead of being pressed against the backs of their couches, they are now able to float about the Apollo cabin at will, standing on their heads as comfortably as they stand on their feet.

There is no "up" and no "down." It matters not whether they fly with their heads toward earth, backward, forward, or sideways. Out the windows, the view of the earth is spectacular. Even at 100 miles up, it is easy to see the curvature of the horizon.

But there is no time to play tourist, to enjoy the breathtaking sight or the thrill of circling the planet in an hour and a half. As soon as the spacecraft reaches orbit, the astronauts remove their gloves and helmets and start to work, preparing for another launch even more critical than their blast-off from earth.

They have no more than four and a half hours to check out their ship and assure themselves that it is safe to finally break away from earth's grip and to go hurtling toward the moon.

The astronaut who rides in the center couch is the busiest of the three. It is he who will navigate the spaceship to the moon and back, using the stars for beacons much as mariners have done for centuries.

He floats from his couch, folds it out of the way, and moves down into the belly of the spacecraft to the lower equipment bay. He will stand here during much of the journey to aim a telescope and a sextant at stars selected long before the flight got underway.

As he begins checking out his instruments, his companions

methodically test the spacecraft's communications, controls, and life-support system. With help from Houston, they make sure everything aboard Apollo is functioning perfectly.

In many ways, the most remarkable part of the whole intricate machine is the guidance and navigation system that must steer the spacecraft to its rendezvous with the moon and tell the astronauts where they are every moment. It is capable of getting them home again even if something severs all communication with Houston.

The heart of the system is a package of gyroscopes the size of a basketball suspended in such a way that they maintain a fixed orientation no matter how the spacecraft maneuvers about. Sensitive devices called accelerometers, also in the package, detect every change in the spacecraft's speed—forward, backward, sideways, up, or down.

Measurements made by this "inertial-measurement unit" go directly into Apollo's guidance computer. By knowing the spacecraft's orientation and how much it has accelerated in what direction, the computer can calculate the vehicle's position at any time. When it is told where the spacecraft wants to go in a maneuver, the computer determines which of the vehicle's control thrusters to use and how long to fire them. Unless the astronauts want to take manual control and fly the spacecraft like an airplane, the computer fires the thrusters and controls the vehicle.

This sounds extremely complex, and is. This is necessary because there is nothing outside the window to tell pilots exactly which way their spacecraft is pointed.

The third part of the system consists of the telescope and sextant used by the navigator to sight at stars and landmarks on the earth and the moon.

Long before the spacecraft is launched, the positions of the stars and landmarks to be used in navigating through space are recorded in the computer's memory. Using the telescope and sextant to sight on these targets and measure the angles between them, the Apollo navigator is able to tell where the spacecraft is and whether it is on course.

But more importantly, the astronaut uses his sightings to align the spacecraft's inertial gyroscopes properly before every major maneuver. Unless these are properly aligned before the spacecraft fires its engines, it is impossible for them to tell how much the vehicle moves and in what direction. This realignment is necessary from time to time because gyroscopes have an inherent tendency to drift out of their desired orientation as they spin. And much of the time during the Apollo mission, the electrically powered gyroscopes are shut off to conserve power.

So, before every engine firing, the gyroscopes are realigned by the navigator so they can monitor the results of the engine firing. Then, with the information they gather, the guidance computer can orient the spacecraft correctly and determine when to shut off the rocket engine.

The first test flights in the Apollo program showed that the navigational system could determine the spacecraft's location as it moved through space almost as accurately as the computers in the Houston Mission Control Center working with information gathered by gigantic radar tracking antennas on earth.

Through most of two trips around the earth, the command module pilot stands at his station in the lower equipment bay making his initial star and landmark sightings to be sure the spacecraft is aimed correctly when the third-stage Saturn engine fires to send it toward the moon.

As bombardiers took control of World War II bombers when they passed over their targets, the Apollo navigator has a small control handle before him in the lower equipment bay to maneuver the spacecraft and bring his target stars into view of his telescope and sextant.

Probably on the second crossing of the Pacific, the astronauts are ready to head for the moon. The navigator floats from his work station back up to his couch. All the equipment the astronauts have been using is stored, so that nothing can fly dangerously about the cabin as the engine drives the spacecraft ahead with nearly a quarter of a million pounds of thrust.

Even though objects are weightless in space, they still have the same mass that they do on earth. A camera, for example, could injure one of the pilots or damage crucial instruments if it were hurled across the cabin by the sudden acceleration.

Because the moon is traveling around the earth at more than 2,000 miles per hour, Apollo aims well ahead of it, at the spot where the moon will be in three days. In effect, the moon and the spacecraft fly to a rendezvous with each other.

Leaving a huge plume of white-hot flame behind it, the Saturn third-stage rocket pushes Apollo for more than five minutes, driving its speed from 18,000 miles per hour to more than 25,000 miles per hour before the engine shuts off, leaving the spacecraft to coast the rest of the way to the moon.

Almost from the moment the rocket engine shuts off, the spacecraft begins gradually to slow down. With earth's gravity tugging at it, Apollo coasts slower and slower until it comes within the gravitational field of the moon. As the moon's gravity begins to pull at it, Apollo speeds up again.

While it plunges through space near its top speed, the astronauts begin their most difficult assignment.

The spacecraft separates from the rocket stage and edges about 100 feet away from it. Then it turns completely around, so the astronauts are looking back at the rocket stage still carrying the spiderlike moon landing vehicle. Panels, which have surrounded the landing vehicle until now, are hurled away by powerful springs, leaving the lunar module exposed. The astronauts make their spacecraft creep slowly back toward the landing vehicle, maneuvering by hand instruments so that antennas stay pointed at the earth to maintain communication with the Mission Control Center, The astronaut in the left seat makes the approach by manipulating a control handle just as a pilot flies an airplane by moving a control stick in the direction he wants to move.

Inch by inch, even though both vehicles are moving some 400 miles per minute, the astronaut steers his ship to the landing vehicle. They touch, and 12 powerful latches automatically engage, locking the command module and lander together.

The pilots then hook up electrical connections to feed power from the command craft into the landing vehicle during the rest of the journey to the moon.

When the intricate docking maneuver is completed, a signal from the cockpit fires explosive charges to sever the landing vehicle's connection to the rocket stage, and springs shove the docked spacecraft away. The Apollo spacecraft fires short bursts from its control engines, backing farther away from the expended rocket stage so there is no chance of collision.

The moon vehicle is now finally assembled.

The astronauts are some 10,000 miles from earth, but joining up with their landing vehicle does not mean that they can now settle down and enjoy the ride. The time is fast approaching for their first mid-course correction, so the navigator must get back to his station below the crew couches and start making his star sightings.

With good fortune, only a small nudge from the command craft's main rocket engine will sharpen their path toward the moon enough that another change in course will not be required until they are almost there.

It already has been a long day. The astronauts were up before dawn at their crew quarters in Kennedy Space Center's Manned Space Operations Building. A final medical examination had been made earlier. They had joined for breakfast a few of the men who had done the most to prepare for this day. The breakfast had been the same that every space pilot launched by the United States ate before he headed for his spacecraft—filet mignon and eggs.

They had pulled on their heavy space suits, hooked up portable air conditioners to keep them comfortable, and walked out into the television floodlights and the applause of workers who had come to see them off. They then had begun their long journey, riding to the launch pad in a windowless white van that looked like a milk delivery truck.

All that is far behind.

The mid-course correction done, the astronauts now put their spaceship into cruising attitude. Curiously, they do not fly straight ahead. Rather, they go into a slow rolling maneuver,

How Apollo and Earth Speak to Each Other

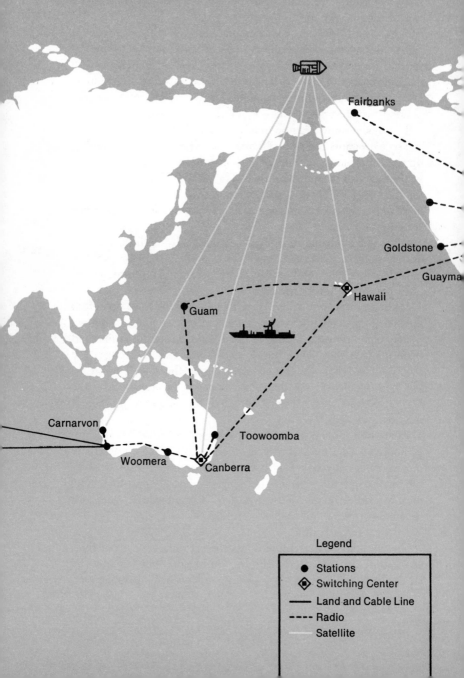

Fairbanks

Goldstone

Guayma

Hawaii

Guam

Carnarvon

Woomera

Canberra

Toowoomba

Legend

● Stations
◈ Switching Center
—— Land and Cable Line
- - - Radio
—— Satellite

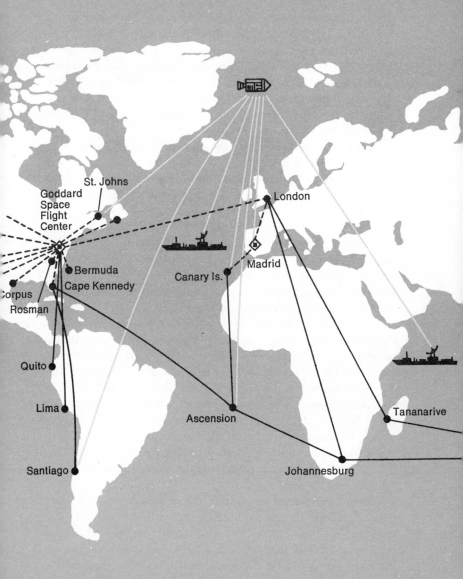

which Apollo engineers long ago labeled the "barbecue mode."

They will actually see very little of the moon until they go into orbit 69 miles above its surface. On the way, the spacecraft will keep gently rolling, turning about two times each hour so that the heat from the sun will be evenly distributed. Otherwise, the delicate control rockets and other sensitive equipment would become too hot on the side facing the sun and too cold in the shadow.

Now, for the first time since they boarded the spacecraft back on earth, their flight to the moon settles into a routine. There is time for the astronauts to eat and to slip into sleeping bags behind their couches, zipping themselves in so that they won't float about the cabin.

If there is no problem to be studied, Apollo can be left alone to fly itself. At least one pilot wears earphones so Houston can call to wake him, if necessary. It is not easy to sleep the first night in space, but they must try. The hardest part of the mission is still ahead. They know that, before the mission is over, fatigue will become one of their major concerns.

They are bound for one of the smooth seas along the moon's equator where it is early morning. Planners for Project Apollo, using photographs returned from Ranger, Lunar Orbiter, and Surveyor, had approved five landing sites in an "Apollo zone" on the moon many months before the first Apollo flight. The sites had to be in the equatorial zone so that the spacecraft could be launched on a "free-return trajectory." After it passes behind the moon, a vehicle on such a course will automatically curve back to earth solely under the influence of earth's gravity. This is insurance against going past the moon and being lost in orbit around the sun.

The sites are spread across the equator because it is necessary to land where the early morning sun will be casting long shadows, making it possible for astronauts to see craters and boulders easily. If they tried to land where it is noontime on the moon, it would be extremely dangerous. The glare of the sun makes it impossible to see details. It is almost like looking down at an endless expanse of snow under glaring sunlight. In addition, the heat is too great to withstand.

With the five sites spaced across the moon, it is possible to select one where the lighting conditions are correct on the day of arrival.

Early in their third day, now more than 175,000 miles from earth, the astronauts and their spacecraft fall under the gravitational attraction of the moon. Apollo is now moving less than 3,000 miles per hour, but it starts to accelerate, picking up speed faster and faster as it moves toward the moon. By the time Apollo gets there it will be moving more than 5,000 miles per hour.

During the first half of the journey, the navigator looked back toward earth, sighting at stars and the earth's horizon to calculate the spacecraft's position, but now he uses landmarks on the moon itself, along with stars, to be sure that they are on course.

After reaching the moon's sphere of gravitational influence, the astronauts make another mid-course correction. With the information the navigator has collected on the way, and the continuous tracking with telescopes back on earth, it is now possible to steer the vehicle precisely into the slot they must enter as they sweep past the front side of the moon.

Their last major maneuver made, the astronauts get their final chance for a rest before they go into the most demanding phase of their entire voyage.

They make their spine-tingling rendezvous with the moon flying backward, aiming just ahead of it as it passes their left, so big now that it fills the sky, a barren, lifeless thing nothing like the familiar white crescent seen from earth.

The spacecraft is going backward so that its rocket engine will act as a powerful brake when it is fired, slowing the Apollo enough that it will become captured in orbit 69 miles above the surface.

If the engine misfires during the braking maneuver and refuses to restart, the only way the men in the Apollo cabin can get back to earth is to fire the landing engine of the lunar module while the two vehicles are still docked, shoving them out of their lunar orbit and on their way home.

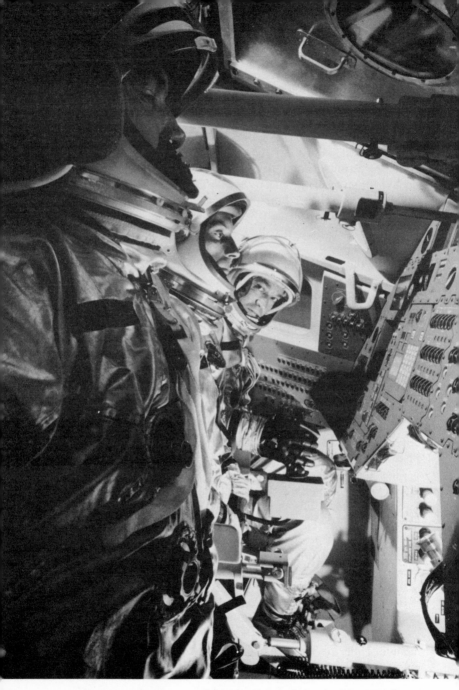

Engineers conducting one of the countless tests involved in preparing an Apollo spacecraft for a trip to the moon.

The astronauts—too busy to be intimidated by the moon looming outside their window—call out their last reports to Houston. In a flash they disappear behind the moon, out of all radio or tracking contact with earth.

For the first time since they climbed into their spacecraft, the astronauts are entirely on their own.

In the Mission Control Center back on earth, flight controllers begin a long half-hour wait. Not until Apollo swings around the other side of the moon will they know whether it is in orbit.

Flying upside down, the lunar craters sweeping beneath them, the astronauts are under control of their spacecraft computer. Some five minutes after they disappear, the vehicle is positioned for its engine firing. Just as countdown clocks in Florida ticked off the last seconds before launch, the computer counts down the last seconds before the crucial maneuver.

Five seconds before ignition, it asks the crew whether all is well to go ahead. The commander pushes a "proceed" key on his computer keyboard, and the spacecraft rocket starts firing.

Success!

Caught in orbit, the spacecraft circles the moon three times during a period of five and a half hours.

The navigator is again at his station working with his telescope and sextant. The earth-based tracking system is also following the spacecraft as it passes in front of the moon. Together they pinpoint its precise path as the spacecraft commander and the landing craft pilot remove a hatch leading to a tunnel connecting the command module and landing vehicle. They clear docking equipment out of the tunnel and the landing craft pilot crawls through, headfirst, into the taxi.

It is the first time he has been inside the landing vehicle since it was checked out on earth. Now he must find out whether it is still functioning well enough to risk separation from the command module and descent to the moon.

Shortly after the landing craft's pilot enters, the spacecraft commander, who will go to the moon with him, crawls through the tunnel. They check the engines, the electrical power, the navigation equipment, and the environmental-control system.

Of all the design, engineering, and manufacturing work preparing for a landing on the moon's surface, development of the
landing craft was perhaps the most difficult. The vehicle is
radically different from any other flying machine ever built. It
is designed to operate exclusively where there is no atmosphere.

Unlike the Saturn rocket and the main Apollo spacecraft, it
is an ugly, angular thing, devoid of the streamlining of high-
speed airplanes, spacecraft, and missiles.

But the landing craft doesn't need streamlining, because it
flies where there is no air. If it is shaped like anything familiar
at all, the taxi can be said to resemble a boulder with legs and
four club feet. Actually, it is two different vehicles in one—a
landing stage for going down to the surface from lunar orbit,
and a take-off stage to carry the two astronauts back to orbit
to join their fellow astronaut waiting in the command craft. It
stands some 22 feet, 11 inches tall, measures 14 feet across, and
on earth weighs 16 tons.

Limiting the weight of the landing craft was one of the
engineers' most persistent problems, even though the vehicle
is fashioned of an extremely light, high-strength aluminum alloy.
To save weight, it was designed without seats. The two astronauts land and take off from the moon standing up, peering
through two tiny windows.

On the way down, they can throttle the craft's descent rocket,
much as an airplane pilot adjusts the power of his jet engines.
The moon lander maneuvers like a helicopter as it approaches
its target, hovering on its jets if necessary.

In an emergency, it can land on a fairly steep incline without
toppling. It is supposed to touch the surface very gently, but its
flat feet are designed of a crushable metal honeycomb to absorb
the shock of a rough landing.

On takeoff, the lower stage, which brings it down to a landing, is used as a launching pad. The vehicle literally splits in
two. A guillotinelike device severs the electrical lines connecting the two stages as a lifting engine carries the crew compartment back into space. The descent engine and the landing gear
are left behind forever on the moon.

But this comes later. Before the lunar landing, the astronauts move scientific equipment and supplies for their stay on the moon through the tunnel, then close the airlock between the two vehicles, leaving the navigator alone in the command craft.

Using the taxi's small thrusters, the astronauts unhook from the command craft and ease 60 feet away, pitching their craft into an upright position so that the lone astronaut in the command module can peer through his window and see whether their landing gear is extended.

Gradually, they drift far enough apart for tests of the rendez-vous radar system that will bring the two vehicles back together

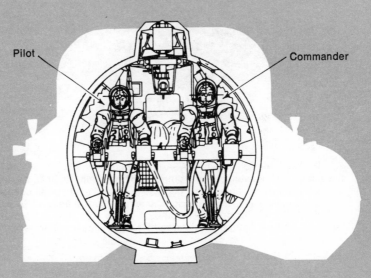

How They Ride in the Lunar Taxi

Pilot

Commander

Seats were eliminated from the lunar taxi to save weight. Astronauts stand while riding the lander to and from the moon's surface.

Where Our Men Land on the Moon

Five landing sites selected by NASA for setting down our astronauts on the moon are all located on the visible side of the moon within 45 degrees east and west of its center and 5 degrees north and south of its equator. In choosing these sites from among 30 originally considered, NASA took into account such factors as smoothness of the area (few craters and boulders) and the approach (no large hills, high cliffs, or sharp slopes).

No.	Coordinates	Location
1	34°E, 2°40′N	Sea of Tranquillity
2	23°37′E, 0°45′N	Sea of Tranquillity
3	1°20′W, 0°25′N	Central Bay
4	36°25′W, 3°30′S	Ocean of Storms
5	41°40′W, 1°40′N	Ocean of Storms

after the visit to the moon's surface.

Again behind the moon, the landing vehicle fires its descent engine, starting it into a coasting fall toward its target, a smooth area near the equator where the morning sun is just rising, casting long shadows across the rough landscape.

The shallow landing descent continues for an hour as both spaceships circle the moon. The landing craft goes down to 50,000 feet while the pilots and controllers back on earth decide whether to fire the descent engines again and go down further.

At this height, the astronauts in the lunar module can still be rescued by the command module if they encounter an emergency.

Given the go-ahead to continue their step-by-step progress toward landing, they fire the descent engine again, burning it for almost eight minutes as they travel 250 miles and approach within less than 9,000 feet of the surface. They are now 8 miles from their landing site. They see it for the first time as the pilot pitches the vehicle so that they are looking down at the surface through their windows.

Cutting power to 60 percent, they move slowly forward and downward to an altitude of just 500 feet, reporting every detail to Houston as they maneuver the craft. They are close enough now to see whether the landing site is as safe as it looked from orbit.

The spacecraft pitches upright again, the flame from the descent engine blossoming out into the vacuum of empty space, as the lander hovers for more than a minute.

The tension on earth is nearly unbearable as the Mission Control Center describes the agonizingly slow descent. Most of the world is following every move as the two astronauts travel the last 100 feet.

They have no fear that the craft will disappear into a deep layer of dust, as some scientists once suggested, but they want the final touchdown to be as delicate as they can make it.

The engine churns up dust that has been undisturbed for billions of years. The pilots feel their engine firing beneath their feet and hear it in the cockpit, but outside on the moon there is not a sound as the ship from another world inches down.

Metallic probes sticking out from the bottom of the space-craft's landing pads touch the surface. They trigger a warning light in the cabin, telling the pilots they are 5½ feet from the moon. A split second later they cut off the engine. The lunar taxi falls the last few inches, coming to rest with a thump.

It is a crowning moment of history.

CHAPTER SIX

Exploring the Moon

Man arrives on the moon knowing a great deal about what confronts him, but relatively little about his ability to cope with it.

The first few trips to the moon might be described as "limited exploration"—scouting expeditions to tell us how difficult it will be to establish a foothold, to begin studying the moon's more interesting and less accessible geological features, and to set up shelters where men can live in some comfort while they work.

The first astronauts to land are under strict orders to stay close to the landing vehicle, to take no chances on becoming overly tired, and to be attentive to the landing craft, which must launch them back into space.

The initial landings on the moon have been made as simple as possible. They are taking place in the smoothest, most level areas to be found. They are being carried out close to the equator so that the rendezvous with the command ship can be carried out quickly without pushing either spacecraft to the limits of its performance.

The orbiting command module passes directly over the landing craft parked on the moon so the rendezvous can be made with a minimum of maneuvering.

Apollo 11 Lunar Module Pilot Edwin E. Aldrin (left) practices picking up samples of moon soil with a specially designed scoop while Spacecraft Commander Neil Armstrong photographs the scene. Their lunar landing craft is in the background.

The first explorers on the moon are like pilots flying an experimental airplane. They alone decide what they should do and how far they should go, so long as they go not a step beyond their approved plan. They try to follow instructions to the letter, but if they decide on a change, it is always supposed to be on the conservative side, in favor of safety.

Before they pay any attention to the strange place where they have landed, they carefully inspect their landing craft to make sure that it has survived the touchdown without damage and that all its systems are working perfectly before they depressurize their cabin and prepare to open the door.

At first, only one astronaut ventures outside to check the exterior of the vehicle, the landing gear, and the surface of the immediate landing area. He unfolds a small antenna which makes it possible for the astronauts to communicate with earth while they are outside the vehicle.

Step by step, the explorers go through their assignments, performing the most important things first, so these will be out of the way in the event that they become exhausted, develop trouble with their moon suits, or have to hurry back aboard their craft for some reason.

The primary assignment is to grab a sample of moon dust. The first man out stops at the foot of the landing craft stairs and scoops the dust into a plastic bag. The visitors from earth move cautiously, stiffly, like science fiction robots. It is as though they were learning to walk all over again, balancing themselves carefully and stopping frequently to rest. They carry tools to jab into the ground to get samples of moon soil; long-handled grapplers make it possible for them to pick up rocks without bending very much.

On their backs, they carry heavy packs which pressurize their suits, cool their bodies against the heat of the morning sun, and furnish them with oxygen to breathe. If they bend over too far, the packs throw them off balance. If they fall, they have great difficulty getting up again. A broken helmet would mean instant death.

The dust underfoot is powder-fine. As far as the astronauts

can see, there is nothing but dust, rock, and craters, their rims
rising up on the horizon. It is hot and still and silent, a frightening place, unlike anything human eyes have ever seen before.
It is nearly impossible to tell how big things are or how far
away they are. The only guidemarks are the sun, the stars,
and the long shadows cast across the rocks and craters. Never
have two men been so alone, so dependent on their wits and
on the reliability of their equipment.

Before the first flights to the moon, planners were not even
sure how difficult it would be to walk on its surface. Some
scientists expected astronauts to be able to leap about like
kangaroos as soon as they got accustomed to the moon's weak
gravity. Others expected that it would be as difficult to move
about as it is for astronauts to work while floating outside an
orbiting spacecraft because of the lack of traction to gain a
foothold.

For the sake of safety, they assumed the worst. The astronauts on the first landing mission were told to stay within 100
yards of their spacecraft as they set up scientific instruments
and collected 50 pounds of rocks and dust. They were told not
to be outside for more than three hours and to limit their
total time on the surface to less than a day.

Despite these difficulties, scientists expect new, fundamental
knowledge about our planet's satellite, resulting from the use
of Apollo's special instruments. With a small nuclear generator
to provide electrical power and send radio information back
to earth, these instruments measure tremors in the moon's
surface, sample the solar wind—radiation from the sun—and
gauge the rate at which heat is being given off from the interior of the moon.

Because no one knew, initially, how difficult it would be to
work on the moon, astronauts on the first landing mission were
asked to set up only three instruments, all within about 30 feet
of the landing vehicle.

One studies moonquakes. Another samples the solar wind.
The third instrument is nothing more than a reflector to bounce
light beams back to earth after they are fired from earth to

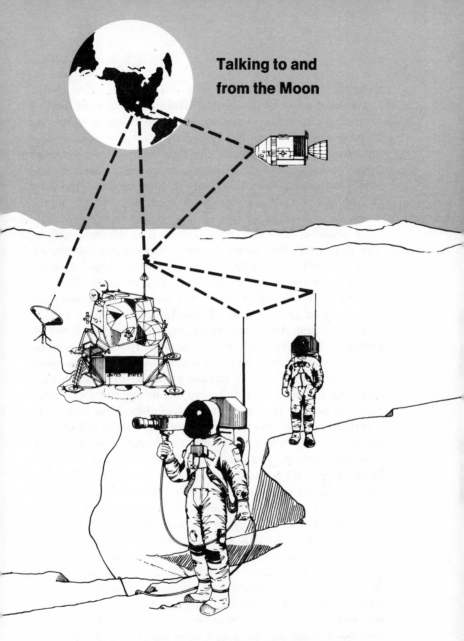

Talking to and from the Moon

Astronauts, on the surface of the moon, speak to each other by radio and keep in touch with earth headquarters at Houston and with their fellow astronaut while he continues circling the moon in the mother ship. Radio also transmits nonvocal data, such as the heartbeats of the astronauts and the results of lunar tests.

the moon by lasers.

The laser is one of the most amazing instruments of modern technology. It produces the most intense beam of light man has ever created. Instead of spreading in all directions as does light from an ordinary bulb, the light from a laser is aimed precisely with all of the light waves traveling along a thin, reedlike channel. Because of this intense focusing, the laser can be beamed all the way from earth to a target on the moon.

By studying how this light is reflected, scientists will be able to measure the moon's distance from earth within inches. They also will learn more about the precise behavior of the earth's tides and how the moon's gravity generates them.

There is an interesting theory that the earth's continents are drifting apart. Look at a world map for a few minutes and try to imagine how Africa and South America could be fitted together if they were pieces of a puzzle. The shapes suggest that they once were a single mass and have since broken apart. According to the theory of continental drift, the continents are still imperceptibly moving away from one another. After scientists have studied laser light reflected from the moon over a period of about 10 years, they should be able to tell whether the continents really are drifting apart, and if so, how fast.

During early exploration, astronauts will also use a simple hand drill to get a piece of the moon's material a few feet beneath the surface. They will drill a 1-inch wide hole perhaps 10 feet deep, and after its core has been extracted, insert a thermometer into it to see how much the subsurface of the moon is insulated by rock and dust on top.

Seismic, or moonquake, studies also have scientific priority. This kind of information will tell whether the moon is "dead" or whether it is still undergoing substantial change because of forces within. Some scientists believe there are as many as five moonquakes a day. Seismometers—moonquake detecting devices—will measure these as well as the impact of substantial meteorites. By studying the way shock waves travel through the moon's crust after a quake, scientists will be able to tell whether the moon has a molten core generated by intense internal pressure, as the earth does, or whether the moon is "lifeless"—just a lump of rock.

One Apollo experiment will set off its own moonquakes. Long after the astronauts have left for home—perhaps a year later—a device will fire four grenades across the moon. One will travel a mile, another 3,000 yards, another 1,000, and the last 500.

Because experimenters will know how far the grenades travel and how much energy they release when they explode on impact, it will be possible for them to get very precise findings about the moon's crust to depths of several thousand feet. They will do this here on earth by reading the data from the seismometers on the moon that will measure the waves spreading through its surface from the exploding grenades.

At one time, it was suggested that the first astronauts on the moon should take off again immediately, without opening the door. There also was a scheme to equip a lander with an automatic pilot, setting it down on the moon without men aboard as a final test before attempting a manned landing. Both were dismissed because officials were confident that astronauts could safely cut short a landing attempt if they met serious difficulty during their approach.

The Apollo system is designed for stays of two or three days. The active lifetime of the landing vehicle is limited because it draws electrical power from storage batteries. Its design pays little attention to astronaut comfort. As mentioned earlier, seats were left out as a weight-saving measure. Moon visitors have to get their sleep lying on the floor or squeezed into hammocks.

It is possible to modify the landing craft so that it might stay on the moon for a week or more, but when visits are extended beyond three days, it probably will be necessary to have an outside shelter to give the explorers better quarters. It is unlikely that much significant exploration can be done so long as astronauts must live in the landing craft.

Even so, it is surprising how much can be done with this small vehicle.

An artist's conception of a future base on the moon, designed to sustain a 12-man crew for 6 months at a stretch while engaging in optical and radio astronomy.

For example, it is possible to pack a moon shelter into a small box which can be stored in the lower portion of the lander—the part that stays on the moon. Made of foam material about 2 inches thick, sandwiched between thin layers of white, plasticlike material, the shelter can be unpacked, then inflated with a small carbon dioxide pellet. This shelter, weighing about 300 pounds and packed into a box measuring 3 by 4 feet, will create a hut 7 feet wide and 20 feet long. It draws power and oxygen from the landing craft and provides two explorers with relative comfort for a stay of several days.

The lander also can carry a small "flyer," or roving vehicle, which would enable astronauts to get about much more ef-

One version of the kind of vehicle our astronauts may be using in the future to get around faster and farther on the moon. This model, developed by Grumman, has a 7-mile radius of operation at a speed up to 10 miles an hour.

fectively than on foot. This tiny, rocket-powered flyer, on which a single astronaut would stand, could zip over the surface at more than 60 miles per hour, delivering its passenger to crater floors or into otherwise inaccessible highland areas. It would enable explorers to avoid wasting time simply getting to places they want to investigate.

A compact wheeled vehicle also could be carried to the moon inside the descent portion of the space taxi. Geologists, particularly, favor such surface transportation. They want a vehicle that can stop every few feet to pick up samples. The flyer would be used more effectively for sending an astronaut to a single site where he could work for a period and then speedily return.

By making more than one voyage to the same landing site on the moon, we could collect in one spot enough equipment for fairly serious exploration and research. A crude moon station could be started by using robot landing craft as supply ships. An unmanned lunar taxi, for example, might carry 6 tons of supplies.

However, scientists first want to secure a basic knowledge about the moon before considering long visits. They prefer using each lunar craft for exploring a different place rather than wasting some as supply ships. Some two dozen lunar features of special interest have been selected, and scientists feel that about 10 of them are important enough to justify separate manned landings. They want to send astronauts into the lunar highlands, where the moon's virgin material may be exposed on the surface. They are interested in landing in both old and new craters, in areas where there is evidence of volcanic activity, and in places where it appears that streams of water or lava once flowed.

Near the lunar North Pole, there are craters where the sun has never shone, because it never gets high enough in the sky to light their floors. There is speculation that these pitch-black craters might be so cold as to hold frozen remains of a long-lost atmosphere. Traces of a moon atmosphere might provide another key to an understanding of the history of the solar

A lunar industrial complex, such as the one envisaged in this drawing, may some day extract liquid hydrogen, oxygen, and other propellants from rocks found on the moon. Some engineers predict that the cost of producing these materials will be economically feasible by the year 2001.

system.

The bottoms of lunar craters also would make excellent locations for telescopes to look for entire galaxies new to man. Much has been said about the possibility of erecting giant radio telescopes on the back side of the moon, where they would be totally shielded from interference from earth.

Though many engineers favor a seemingly risky landing on the back side of the moon with the lunar taxi, this is not likely in the near future. As mentioned, a spacecraft on the far side of the moon is out of all communication with earth. Officials would not now permit a manned spacecraft to land where the astronauts would be out of contact.

To get around this problem, an Apollo spacecraft circling the moon before sending a landing craft down to the surface might pitch out its own communications satellites. These, orbiting the moon, would make it possible for explorers on the back side to maintain nearly constant communication with Houston.

All of these steps are possible, using equipment developed for the initial lunar landings.

To explore the moon's polar regions and the highland areas far from the equator, space planners will have to give up one of the fundamental safety valves built into their flights: the free-return trajectory.

The "free return" path carries the vehicle into a moon orbit around the equatorial zone. Whenever planners are so confident as to give up this safety valve, they will be able to go into various orbits for landings anywhere they choose.

Scientists want very much to wander afar because the lunar seas selected for initial landings are not so interesting geologically as areas where there is evidence of volcanic activity or of outcroppings of material as old as the moon itself. Future spacecraft will be equipped to drill deep into the surface to find material that has not been changed by volcanic activity or meteorite impact.

Development of drills which will work on the surface of the moon is a difficult technical task. Because water is not available and because there is no air to cool them, drills wear out fast.

So, planners have modified their once-ambitious plans to drill deep into the surface. They hope, however, to be able to drill deep enough to get into the bedrock beneath the lunar seas.

As exploration progresses, astronauts will be able to make some preliminary chemical and geological analyses of samples they collect on the surface. Thus, they could be selective in their digging, gathering only material of first-rate scientific value.

Scientific instruments left on the moon by the early teams of explorers will send back information which will help scientists decide where they wish to go next and possibly where the first semipermanent scientific stations should be located.

Seismometers deployed in a triangular pattern will not only permit the measurement of quakes but also will pinpoint places where the quakes take place. With this information, scientific missions can be dispatched to areas where the moon's crust may even now be shifting and changing and where landslides are filling in the floors of ancient craters.

The rate of moon exploration will depend largely on how frequently landings are made. Scientists would like to launch about two flights a year. These would give them enough time between flights to digest the information from previous expeditions and decide where to send the next. Flight operations officials would like to send men to the moon frequently because astronauts, flight controllers, and engineers then would stay at a high state of training.

NASA's plan for exploring the moon is divided into three periods: (1) preliminary observation and discovery, (2) exploration, and (3) comprehensive investigation. The last will include a search for resources on the moon which could be used to support permanent scientific stations or colonies.

Moon dust itself will be a valuable resource when explorers, tunneling beneath the surface, use it to cover their living quarters and laboratories to insulate them against the glaring sun.

Special facilities will have to be developed for growing food and for bringing water up from the subsurface or extracting

it from the moon's rock. Power stations will have to be set up.
All this will be expensive and will require numerous flights to
the same landing site. Scientists and engineers will have to
sample several places on the moon to decide where to build
a permanent station.

Discovery of water in usable form beneath the moon's surface would obviously solve a major problem. It would also
create new interest in biological investigation. Where there is
moisture, there is reason to suspect there is, or has been, life.

In summary, the pace of development on the moon will be
determined by how fast man learns to use what he finds there.
So long as it is necessary to carry all the equipment for every
expedition, the pace of exploration will be slow. Lack of on-site
resources is the reason man has been slow to conquer the polar
areas on earth.

If rocket fuel can be produced from materials on the moon,
this would be a great step forward. It would enable spaceships
to deliver large numbers of men and great amounts of cargo
from the earth. Large ships bound for the moon would not have
to carry with them fuel for the return trip, and space would
be liberated for passengers and cargo.

A lunar fuel station would also bring closer the day when
the moon may serve as a launching pad for manned expeditions
to the outer reaches of the solar system—perhaps to go into
orbit around Jupiter or land on one of its moons. A space
vehicle launched from the moon must reach a speed of only
about 5,000 miles per hour to escape its gravity. This means
that huge spaceships could be launched from the moon with
a fraction of the energy required to launch them from earth.

Such are the vistas which open to man during the final decades of this century.

CHAPTER SEVEN

Returning to Earth

Their work on the moon completed, the two astronauts now begin one of the most hazardous operations of the entire lunar mission. They must lift off in the small taxi to rejoin the main spacecraft in orbit around the moon. They must rise from the lunar desert by means of a single engine, with only their own skills and radio advice from Houston, 240,000 miles away, to supplement the calculations of their small, on-board computer.

After checking out the engine and controls, they await the next passage of the mother ship. As this ship and its lone pilot come over the horizon, the two moon explorers fire the taxi's ascent engine.

For 12 seconds, the upper part rises straight up. Gathering speed, the box-shaped taxi tilts and begins pursuit of the main spacecraft.

For more than six minutes, the rocket engine blazes away, as the taxi hurtles to a speed of more than 1 mile per second. Standing shoulder-to-shoulder at the control panel, the astronauts can now see a broader and broader expanse of the lunar landscape.

As the engine shuts off, the taxi has reached a height of 50,000 feet. It is now coasting in an orbit which will carry it as high as 30 miles.

Another of the most critical milestones is behind the astronauts. Had their ascent engine failed to start, they would have been trapped on the moon, beyond hope of rescue. As soon as their oxygen supply ran out, they would have suffocated. The navigator waiting for them in the orbiting spacecraft would have had no choice but to start home alone, because he could not have gone down to the moon to save them.

But now, in orbit beneath the path of the mother ship, the two moon explorers have reached a midway point. Should their engine fail them here, they have at least attained an altitude where they can be rescued by the pilot in the other craft.

Some 350 miles behind the mother ship, the astronauts in the taxi are zeroing in on their target with radar. At the same time, both vehicles are being tracked back on earth as computers in Houston help the astronauts determine what steps to take to bring the two ships together. They keep to their 30-mile altitude for half an hour while deciding exactly which way to move and how much to accelerate to bring their complex little ship into an orbit that will intercept the command spacecraft.

From now on, they maneuver the taxi by firing small control jets mounted on the sides of the vehicle rather than by using the ascent engine again.

As they flash behind the moon, out of sight of earth, they fire the control jets faster so that the ship swings into an orbit about 15 to 20 miles beneath the path of the command spacecraft. They are closing in and are now only about 50 miles away.

Coming back into view of the earth, the two astronauts make their final maneuver, setting the taxi on a course that will enable it to catch up with the main craft after coasting half way around the moon again.

Three miles from their target, they start slowing the taxi, closing in gingerly so that there will be no chance of a collision.

They edge up to their target, maneuvering within a few

feet—so close that they can now see their companion watching them through his window. If they are on the night side of the moon when they catch up, they will wait until they fly back into daylight before docking. If there is some reason to hurry, however, they can dock in darkness. The docking apparatus is luminescent, and the command spacecraft is equipped with spotlights.

The taxi is moved in gently, and the two ships are docked.

Now the crewmen open the airlock in each of the vehicles, and the landing team starts passing its equipment and precious boxes of moon samples into the command ship.

They carefully brush off everything they put aboard the command craft for the trip home because they want no dust from the moon floating around their cabin, possibly fouling delicate electrical equipment and causing dangerous malfunctions during the flight. Sample boxes and tools used for working on the moon are wrapped in plastic bags, and moon suits are stored away in boxes.

The crew commander and the moon lander pilot worm their way through the tunnel for reunion with the command ship navigator.

The fate of Apollo and the three men aboard still rests with the rocket engine that must take them home.

Before they fire this engine for the return trip, the astronauts must get rid of the taxi. An explosive charge sends it off into space. The astronauts watch carefully to make sure that there is no danger of running into it.

There is no way to take the taxi home because it has no heat shield. It would burn to metallic slag during the fiery reentry. So it will continue floating around the moon alone, perhaps forever. Or perhaps gravity will finally pull it down and cause it to crash on the lunar surface.

Before starting for earth, Apollo circles the moon a final time. The astronauts get their last instructions from Houston. They take star sightings to make sure they agree with Houston on the spacecraft's position and set up the guidance equipment to start them on an unerring course.

11 Steps
Back to Earth

1. With descent stage as a launch pad, the ascent stage fires for lift-off.

2. Astronauts in taxi rendezvous with orbiting mother ship.

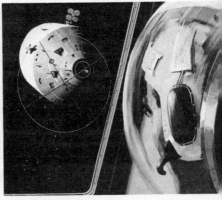

3. Pilot guides taxi to docking with command craft.

4. Astronauts return to mother ship and prepare to abandon taxi in orbit.

5. The command section rocket fires for return to earth.

6. Shortly before reentry, command section jettisons service section.

7. Command craft turns blunt end forward for fiery reentry.

8. Protective shield chars to absorb 5,000-degree heat.

9. Small parachutes open to begin slowing spacecraft.

10. Spacecraft drifts on main parachutes to gentle splashdown.

11. Recovery helicopters move in as craft floats in the ocean, mission completed.

When they fire their engine to start the return trip, the astronauts are passing over the hidden side of the moon and therefore are out of contact with earth, just as they were when they first braked into lunar orbit.

If the engine does not start, the men in Apollo will never get home. Unable to escape the moon's gravity, the crewmen would perish within days. Apollo would suffer the same fate as the discarded lunar taxi.

For many reasons, neither the United States nor Russia has developed a space rescue system. First, such a system would be enormously expensive and would require years to develop. Second, the chances of rescuing a space crew in distress in time to save them would be small. To rendezvous quickly with a stranded spacecraft would require that a rescue rocket be kept fueled on earth and ready for immediate launch.

So, instead of developing a rescue system, the United States has relied on flawless engineering with the hope that failures will not occur in the first place.

The rocket engine for return, above all, must not fail, so engineers designed it as one of the most reliable parts of the whole Apollo system. Although it is normally fired by order from the spacecraft computer, it can be manually turned on and off by the astronauts. It is mounted so that the nozzle can be turned to change the direction of thrust and to control the spacecraft's direction of flight.

It starts when valves open, allowing two different liquids to come into contact with each other. The mixture ignites spontaneously. The engine has no throttles. As soon as it starts, it produces its full 20,500 pounds of thrust. It can be used to carry out very intricate maneuvers, however, because it can be fired for only fractions of a second, if necessary.

Fourteen seconds before the engine starts to speed Apollo toward earth, maneuvering thrusters mounted on the sides of the spacecraft begin firing straight ahead, pushing the main engine's fuel into the bottom of the tanks to feed it as the fuel ignites.

Since the flight began, the spacecraft has used up about two-thirds of its fuel. What remains is drifting about inside the tanks because the spacecraft is weightless. This is why it is necessary to use the small thrust from the control jets to settle the fuel. Once the engine starts, the spacecraft accelerates so rapidly that the fuel is held continuously in the bottom of the tanks while the engine is burning, so there is no need for further assistance from the control jets.

Now is the moment. In darkness, 10 minutes before Apollo swings around the edge of the moon into view of the earth, the commander punches the "proceed" key on his computer keyboard, and seconds later the engine bursts into life.

There is a roar in the cabin, and a solid, comforting thump as the spacecraft surges ahead. Because much of its fuel load has been used, the vehicle is light and the engine shoves it forward with tremendous acceleration. No longer weightless, the astronauts feel themselves pinned to the backs of their couches.

The moon starts falling away below as the astronauts come into daylight and see the earth in the distance, a blue, green, and white gem dominating the sky. The voyagers are more than 200,000 miles from earth and safety, but now it is "downhill" all the way.

The astronauts see the earth grow larger as the spacecraft coasts slower and slower.

After they have made sure that their ship is functioning well, they put it back into its slow rolling maneuver to distribute the sun's heat and then try to fall asleep.

The next day their job is mostly "housekeeping." Slowed to less than a mile per second, the spacecraft reaches the earth's gravitational influence 33,800 miles out from the moon. The crew of Apollo can't detect the change, but from this moment on, they start flying faster and faster as they are pulled toward the earth.

The only concerns now are to keep the life-support equipment working properly, to take navigational sightings, and to get ready for the dramatic end of their journey when the spacecraft, blazing in at 25,000 miles per hour, plunges into

The earth, as seen from the window of a moon ship, is a beautiful agate, spinning in space. Here both sides of the Atlantic Ocean and the bulge of West Africa are visible. Clouds cover the eastern coast of South America.

the earth's atmosphere.

As it dives into the top of the earth's atmosphere, Apollo must hit an imaginary entry "window" about 40 miles wide. If the approach is too shallow, the vehicle can bounce off the atmosphere like a flat rock skipping on water and then go right on past the earth.

On the other hand, if the descent is too steep, the forces of deceleration would be more than the structure of the spacecraft could stand. The protective heat shield could be burned away quickly by the tremendous friction from the air, and the pilots incinerated just thousands of feet above the surface of the ocean.

In reality, finding this narrow window is not so fearsome as it sounds. Midway in the flight home, Apollo has been followed so closely by tracking stations that ground controllers know without doubt that it is on the right path.

If the departure from the moon is normal, the pilots will probably make only two small mid-course adjustments during their flight home. The last comes just two hours before the spacecraft hits the atmosphere, altering its speed only slightly.

Streaking toward earth at a distance of 2,500 miles and still picking up speed, the astronauts get ready to land.

They separate the command spacecraft from the service section—the barrel-shaped part which contains the Apollo engine, the power-generating fuel cells, and other support equipment. These are no longer needed.

The service section is guided away from the command spacecraft's flight path so that it does not interfere with the landing. Eventually, it will reenter the atmosphere and burn.

Now the Apollo command capsule is flying backward. The blunt end of the cone-shaped spacecraft starts encountering the upper reaches of the earth's atmosphere at an altitude of about 400,000 feet. In the next few minutes, the temperature on the heat shield will rise to several thousand degrees, and as Apollo descends, it will become a manned comet, with a tail of fire streaming behind it for miles.

The heat is so intense that it would melt most metals, but

the heat shield is designed of many layers of materials to keep the cabin at a fairly comfortable temperature. The outer layers are made of a substance which, as it burns away, carries the heat with it, instead of allowing the spacecraft to absorb it. While plunging into the thickening atmosphere, Apollo is surrounded by a sheath of superheated gas which radio waves cannot penetrate.

Twenty-five seconds after they first reach the atmosphere, all radio contact with the astronauts is lost for about three minutes until the spacecraft is through the worst part of its descent.

Apollo is now flying under automatic control, its computers issuing commands to small control jets as the pilots monitor their progress, ready to take manual control if anything goes wrong with the automatic system. Although it has no wings, the spacecraft is designed so that it can slow its descent, and even climb briefly to allow cooling, if necessary.

The path through the atmosphere is like the route of a roller coaster. After the temperature has reached 5,000 degrees or so and the spacecraft has dived to 180,000 feet, it begins climbing again, gaining as much as 40,000 to 50,000 feet. This permits it to cool before starting downward again.

Before the astronauts turn upward to cool off, they are being subjected to a force nearly 7 times the normal pull of gravity. That means that a pilot who weighs 160 pounds is being pressed against the back of his couch with a force of almost 1,120 pounds.

At the same time it is plunging downward, the command ship is being rolled by its control thrusters. The spacecraft is designed so that its center of gravity is not at the center of the spacecraft itself. In effect, the vehicle is heavier on one side than it is on the other. Rolling the spacecraft and changing the position of its center of gravity makes it possible to increase or decrease its rate of descent.

At 23,000 feet, small stabilizing parachutes are released. By now the astronauts are in radio contact with recovery ships, and helicopters are already on their way to the point where Apollo

How Man Survives 5,000°
Reentering the Atmosphere

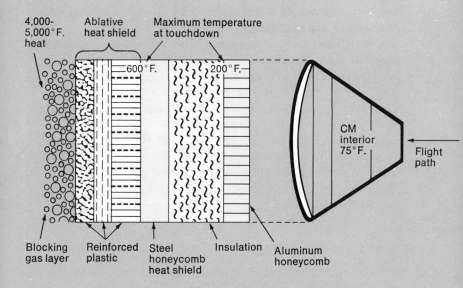

One of the most difficult problems in sending a man to the moon is getting him back through the earth's atmosphere. As a capsule moves through the atmosphere at speeds up to 25,000 miles per hour, the temperature of its surface soars to 5,000 degrees. Unprotected, the metal of the capsule would melt. A major problem in designing a manned spacecraft has been to develop a shield which will insulate the capsule and keep the temperature of the interior low enough for the astronauts to survive. The solution is an "ablative heat shield"—a type of reinforced plastic, only ¾-inch thick, which melts into a gassy layer and floats away, carrying much of the heat with it. Below the exterior layers are materials which absorb the remaining heat, leaving the astronauts insulated in reasonable comfort.

will splash into the sea, home at last.

The small chutes are detached at 10,000 feet. Then three gigantic orange and white parachutes, measuring 77 feet across, pop out and cut down the spacecraft's landing speed.

The astronauts ride the 6-ton craft into the water at 22 miles per hour, sending up a high splash. An aircraft carrier speeds to the scene and lifts the spacecraft aboard.

Unless there is an emergency, the astronauts cannot so much as open the door for a breath of fresh air. They are now under control of scientists who have for years been planning an elaborate system for making sure that moon voyagers do not bring back some bizarre kind of microscopic life that could cause disease or damage crops.

On the aircraft carrier, a plastic tunnel is erected between the spacecraft door and a van the size of a house trailer. The astronauts move through the sealed tunnel into the van, and the door closes behind them. A doctor and a technician wait inside. The physician begins a series of meticulous physical

Returning visitors from the moon must clear quarantine before being released to move about freely on earth. After splashdown, they enter this isolation van, in which they are moved to NASA's Lunar Receiving Laboratory at Houston for more extensive examination.

examinations, and the technician takes charge of their moon samples.

Repackaged in new, sterile plastic bags, the samples are passed out of the van through an airlock. They are put aboard a plane which takes off on the first leg of a flight to Houston, where scientists wait to begin preliminary analyses of the material they hope will tell them much about the origin of the solar system.

In port, the van, with the three astronauts, the physician, and the technician, is removed from the ship and hauled to an airfield where an Air Force plane is waiting to take off for Houston.

Only a few hours after their splashdown, the astronauts land at Ellington Air Force Base, near the Houston Manned Spacecraft Center. No one sees them. The van is trucked to the laboratory at the space center where the moon samples were sent a few hours earlier.

The astronauts move through another plastic tunnel into quarantine quarters in the laboratory. They will not emerge

This is how rock samples, brought to earth from the moon, are moved on a monorail device into a vacuum-glove chamber for analysis by scientists at NASA's Lunar Receiving Laboratory, Houston.

until doctors are sure they did not pick up viruses or bacteria during their visit to the moon's surface. This will take about three weeks.

Project Apollo, the most expensive, controversial, and difficult engineering project ever undertaken, has fulfilled the goal the United States set for itself in 1961. Man at last has flown to the moon and has returned safely to earth. He has fulfilled the mission set originally by President John F. Kennedy.

And the world will never be the same again.

CHAPTER EIGHT

Space-Age 'Spinoffs'

In the long run, the most beneficial result of the race to the moon may be a better standard of living on earth.

Even if we learn to colonize the moon, mine it for diamonds, and use it as a launch pad to go to other planets, these achievements may not be as important as those we secure from the process of getting to the moon. In other words, by-products of the moon mission—referred to as "spinoffs"—may profit man more than fulfillment of the mission itself.

Project Apollo made a deep psychological impact on the American mind. It expanded our horizons to the extent that it became difficult for us to say that anything was impossible. It set a high standard of achievement by which to measure present and future undertakings.

For example, people began to ask: If we can go to the moon, why can't we solve troublesome problems on earth? Why can't we clear up pollution, cure our decaying cities, untangle our traffic jams, exploit the resources of the sea?

The answer is that we can. And the belief is that we can achieve these things by applying the new scientific and management techniques which got us to the moon. They evolved through a partnership between government and private enterprise.

Collectively, these new techniques are known as "the systems approach." One of the basic principles is to break down vast programs, such as the $24 billion Project Apollo, into numerous distinct segments which can be managed separately. The need to do this is clear when you consider the scope of the operation. At the peak of the Apollo program in 1966, more than 20,000 companies were participating in it. More than 350,000 persons throughout the nation were involved as employees of the various contractors or as scientists and engineers in 200 universities.

The Saturn 5 moon rocket alone was the product of 5,000 different contractors employing 150,000 skilled workers in all parts of the United States.

It is widely recognized that the secret of American success in space is due to management techniques combined with engineering techniques. These have made it possible to take new scientific concepts and quickly translate them into hardware that will perform such miracles as going to the moon.

It is this highly integrated form of industrial and scientific activity, developed to a greater degree than ever before, that has opened the possibility of solving some of man's worst problems on earth.

Karl G. Harr, Jr., President of the Aerospace Industries Association, once said: "There appears to be no limit to the type or complexity of the projects the systems approach can make manageable. Using computer techniques, possible plans can be presented for achieving any given public goal of construction or modernization on a national scale."

At the heart of future progress, of course, lies education. After gaining top priority among national objectives in the early 1960s, the country's space program stimulated U.S. science and engineering education.

One of the first reactions to the Soviets' launch of Sputnik 1 in 1957 was a widespread feeling in the United States that our educational system was behind the times. The Russians appeared to have badly outdistanced us in turning out scientists and engineers. It was the reaction to Soviet space exploits that in large measure stimulated the rapid growth of federal aid to education in the United States.

Pressed for top-rate scientists and engineers, NASA poured money into universities to support graduate education and to back faculty research. It established a program to turn out 1,000 Ph.D.'s each year.

The late Dr. Hugh L. Dryden, one of America's aerospace pioneers, once said that the greatest impact of this country's space exploration was it stimulation of young people to study science and engineering.

NASA, from the start, was active in transferring its know-how to practical use. This has had the effect of stimulating the economy and reducing the time lag between the discovery of new scientific knowledge and its practical application.

The space agency launched a Technology Utilization Program to distribute and publicize advances in technology which might otherwise be lost in the workshops of space contractors or in the offices of government engineers. Contractors were instructed to report their discoveries and innovations. Technical personnel at NASA field centers kept their eyes open for new ideas which might be put to use elsewhere.

By the end of 1968, these efforts resulted in nearly 3,000 brief technical bulletins describing innovations. More than half a million copies were distributed by the Commerce Department. Officials estimate that more than 2,500 technical innovations, of potential application on earth, have emerged from space activity.

In addition to these bulletins, the space agency puts out other publications to make known developments of special interest to medium-sized and small businesses. These publications are distributed to more than 20,000 firms through the Small Business Administration. SBA also sponsors conferences of small business executives to acquaint them with opportunities available as a result of new developments in space.

The space agency gathers reports on aerospace technology from public and private sources throughout the world.

All NASA's reports, numbering about 70,000 a year, are catalogued and stored in computers. They also are summarized and published in two semimonthly journals. They have become an important source of data for American industry.

For example, at Goddard Space Flight Center outside Washington, D.C., the NASA installation responsible for scientific satellite programs, engineers developed a satellite coating which would withstand temperatures as high as 1,300 degrees or as low as 320 degrees below zero.

After one of the technical bulletins described this coating, the space agency received more than 1,000 requests for more information. Eventually, two dozen companies asked for, and received, royalty-free licenses to produce the coating, mostly for use as a commercial paint.

An electromagnetic hammer used in the construction of Saturn 5 causes metal to flow like soft plastic so that it can be shaped, smoothed, and welded without weakening, even at the seams. Considerable use of such hammers is predicted for the automotive, aircraft, construction, and other industries in which sheet metal plays a large part.

NASA has developed scores of new chemical compounds, plastics, and metal alloys with good industrial possibilities. Need for fireproofing the Apollo spacecraft resulted in methods for testing materials that will produce safer draperies, upholstery, mattresses, and other fabrics, including clothing.

A 24-ounce, battery-operated TV camera, no bigger than a pack of king-sized cigarettes, is used to photograph separation of Saturn rocket stages as they burn out and are jettisoned. It is now available in a commercial version for monitoring industrial processes. There are many other potential uses for this miniature marvel.

Computer programs, developed for space at costs ranging from $100,000 to $1 million, are now available for less than $100 for use in large-scale construction and manufacturing.

Development of self-lubricating materials for space now makes it possible to produce ball bearings and other engine parts which will last far longer than those now operating in

The need of economy in space inspired the manufacture of this ultra-miniature television camera. It weighs less than 1½ pounds and measures 1½ inches by 3 inches by 4½ inches.

earth vehicles.

Other examples of spinoff are miniature electronic systems of many types and small but extremely versatile computers such as those aboard Apollo.

The field of medicine is one of the major beneficiaries.

For example, a tough, instantly drying spray was developed to attach tiny sensors to the astronauts' bodies so their heart action could be monitored during the stresses of spaceflight. This innovation has been applied successfully in ambulances for quickly attaching and holding electrodes to the skin of victims of heart attacks or accidents. Through these electrodes, second by second, the patients' conditions are radioed to hospital emergency rooms while ambulances are en route. This advance information enables emergency-room crews to begin vital treatment sooner.

Another outgrowth of this body-monitoring system allows one nurse to monitor up to 100 patients from a central point. She can watch a screen and listen for alarms connected to electronic units that instantly inform her if something goes wrong with heartbeats, blood pressure, metabolisms, temperatures, or breathing of patients.

A tiny instrument invented to measure air pressure on rocket and spacecraft models in wind tunnels is being used experimentally by doctors. It is so small that they can inject it into an artery of a heart patient with a hypodermic needle. Then it travels with the blood to the heart and sends out information that could not be measured in any other way.

A small TV camera developed in the space program can

A hospital patient, using a "sight switch" developed originally for astronauts in space, can summon a doctor simply by moving her eyeballs.

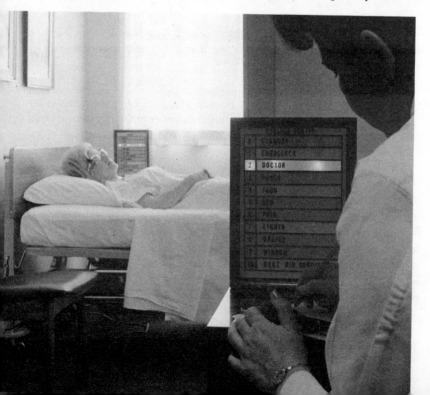

be swallowed to show whether a person has ulcers or other stomach ailments.

Computer techniques worked out to improve photos of Mars and the moon taken by spacecraft are being used to make medical X rays more revealing. In a brain picture, for example, blood vessels stand out as clearly as lines on a map.

A meter used to measure the condition of astronauts' bones after long periods of weightless flight is now being employed to study the brittleness of bones in elderly patients.

For conditions of extreme heat and cold in space, NASA developed highly efficient bearings made of alloys of the versatile metal titanium. Because of their low friction and non-corrosiveness, these bearings are proving very useful in artificial hip, leg, and elbow joints for amputees.

The design of an unmanned, robot instrument-carrier for

A close-up of the "sight switch," designed to enable persons, unable to use their hands or legs, to give commands by moving their eyes. Among possible uses: operation of a machine to turn the pages of a book, to switch lights on and off, to control radio and television sets, to run electric typewriters.

use on the moon has been applied in such a way as to give mobility to paralyzed persons. A person able to move no more than his eyeballs will be able to sit in and control an eight-legged walking vehicle going anywhere he chooses—over street curbs, up stairways, and through mud, sand, snow, or sleet.

NASA scientists working on Project Apollo saw need for an electronic switch that could be controlled simply by moving the eyes to help astronauts if a space problem prevented them from moving.

The answer is a device in which small light sources, mounted on either side of eyeglasses or goggles, bounce threads of light

Development of an unmanned vehicle to carry scientific instruments over the surface of the moon led to creation of this walking chair, which can carry invalids over curbs, climb steps, and operate in sand.

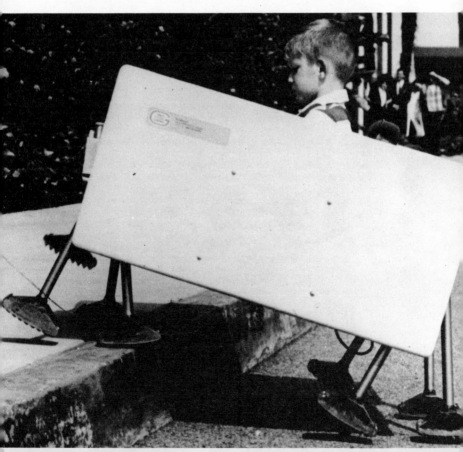

into the wearer's eyes. The light registers the difference between the whites of the eyes and the darker pupils. When the light beam reports pupil movement, electronic switches are activated. They are arranged to set off and control various mechanical motions and other keyed-in reactions. That is the secret of the controls being developed to give mobility to paralyzed persons.

This invention suggests future development of a large variety of devices that might enable us to open or close doors or move almost anything by simply shifting the eyeballs.

A device developed to train astronauts to walk in the moon's low gravity will probably help severely crippled persons learn to walk again.

A highly sensitive instrument designed to measure the impact of microscopic bits of dust against space vehicles has excellent medical possibilities. Because it can detect the slightest muscular tremor, this instrument is being studied for use in the early detection of Parkinson's disease and other neurological ailments.

These and other medical developments from space research are being turned over to the U.S. government's Vocational Rehabilitation Administration for application in everyday life.

The ultrahigh nutritional values of concentrated meals for astronauts developed by NASA experts can be applied to dietary problems of the old and afflicted. Surveys show that many elderly people have deficient diets. Their appetites are small and their digestion not good. Highly balanced and digestible astronaut meals, small in bulk, can help remedy this situation. Such foods could serve equally well for invalids and others with food problems.

There is another possible application of great potential. Because food concentrates can easily be transported, stored, and distributed, either in dry form or in plastic squeeze bottles, they might be used in the future to aid almost half the world's population that is suffering from hunger.

The revolution in communications via satellite is now so well established that extraordinary changes are beginning to be taken for granted, and some people may even be over-looking the fact that they derive from our activities in space.

Satellite transmission of TV pictures now makes it possible for us literally to see events as they take place in London, Paris, and other parts of the world. Satellites also provide us with another way to speak by telephone to the most distant points of the earth. Instant communication via satellite is having the effect of making any point on the globe as close as the one on which we happen to be standing. This is "one world" to an extent hardly dreamed of only a few years ago.

Weather satellites are just beginning to reach their potential. When former President Lyndon B. Johnson was in the Senate and was Chairman of the National Aeronautics and Space Council, he estimated that accurate five-day weather predictions could produce these annual savings in the United States: water-resources management, $3 billion; agriculture, $2.5 billion; surface transportation, $100 million; retail marketing, $75 million; lumber industry, $45 million.

By using satellites in conjunction with other equipment, scientists expect to extend accurate weather forecasts to two weeks. Still further understanding of the weather may eventually enable man to influence its behavior.

Observations of earth resources from space will advance economic development. Satellites will be used for early detection of crop disease, for locating new sources of food and mineral wealth, and for planning irrigation and construction projects.

The engineering establishment of the space age is being relied upon to solve many of the new problems which have arisen in recent years.

We now are planning to build commercial passenger planes which will fly faster than sound. But supersonic airliners will create sonic boom—the thunder which rolls across the earth behind a plane flying faster than sound—and this has become a national issue.

Attention has turned to other sources of noise. And noise, like smoke, or oil dumped into a stream, has come to be regarded as yet another form of pollution.

Engineering techniques perfected in aerospace programs are expected to play an important role in combating pollution, in developing mass-transportation systems, and in producing better hospitals, homes, and schools.

Retired Air Force General Bernard A. Schriever, who played a major role in leading the United States into the missile age, went into business after he left the Air Force, applying space-age management techniques to urban planning.

Some space experts predict that, within a few years, the dividends emerging from our ventures in space will defray the costs of the entire U.S. space program several times over.

And they foresee something even more extraordinary: the setting up of factories on the moon and in space to produce goods of a higher quality than those we can turn out within our earthly environment.

Ball bearings offer an example of what they have in mind. It seems that it is impossible to produce perfect ball bearings on our planet. They suffer from microscopic lumps and craters. Some lightweight, hollow bearings are marked by flaws because they must be made in halves, then carefully welded together and machined. Being imperfect, they wear out quickly in high-speed machinery.

If such bearings could be manufactured on the moon, where gravity is much weaker and less distorting than on earth, they could be produced in one piece as near-perfect spheres. If they could be made where there is no gravity at all—on a manned space station, for example—the ball bearings would form with absolute perfection. Such bearings would last many times longer than any produced on earth.

Orbiting factories in space, made possible by further development of our lunar program, could provide a solution to still other manufacturing problems.

In space it should be possible to grow perfect, giant crystals. These would yield thousands of tiny electronic components such as are used in computers, transistor radios, and television sets. One spaceflight per month might supply the entire world's requirements for such crystals.

Factories free of the harmful effects of gravity could also produce perfect lenses for our glasses, cameras, microscopes, and telescopes. And they could make structural materials with the strength of steel but the weight of balsa wood.

Planners are looking forward to a hugh space station in orbit where these and other ideas might be tried out during the next decade. Should they prove successful, we will be witnessing an extraordinary phenomenon—exports to earth from space and the moon for the greater good of man.

CHAPTER NINE

The First Years of the Moon Race: Mercury

Despite Nazi Germany's development of the V-2 missile as a frightening new weapon, the United States failed to appreciate its full implication—that long-range, strategic rockets, capable of delivering bombs to any point on earth, were almost within reach.

The Soviet Union did. And that, in essence, is what thrust the world into the space age.

After the launch of Sputnik 1 on October 4, 1957, it took the United States years to overcome its miscalculations of the late 1940s and early 1950s.

These miscalculations helped to produce the moon race. Nearly four years after Sputnik, the United States decided that our first real chance to show the world that we could be ahead of the Soviet Union in rocket and space technology would be to beat the Russians to a manned moon landing.

With the benefit of hindsight, it is easy to pinpoint where the United States went wrong at the beginning.

First, we underestimated how fast missile technology would move. We did not anticipate how eagerly the Soviet Union would push into this new field, using captured V-2s to start toward development of longer-range rockets. The United States also experimented with V-2s, but the pace was much slower.

U.S. leaders misjudged how fast new materials, miniature electronics, better triggering devices, and improved yield of warheads would shrink the size of nuclear bombs and make it possible to deliver them with missiles.

They also failed to see how quickly the Russians would rise from the ashes of war to develop their own atomic bomb.

Even after it became clear that both countries could soon launch artificial earth satellites, the United States failed to anticipate the impact of this on people all over the world.

Today it seems almost absurd that we should have lost the lead in space.

In the midst of World War II, the United States carried out the most fantastic scientific-engineering achievement up to that time with the creation of the atomic bomb. At the end of the war, it found itself with most of the top scientists and engineers from the German missile program, including Wernher von Braun, the brain behind the V-2.

But U.S. military men still viewed the missile as an artillery weapon and regarded airplanes with atomic bombs as our main line of strategic defense, extending at least into the middle 1960s.

In December 1945, Dr. Vannevar Bush, the wartime leader of military technology, told a Senate committee: "There has been a great deal of talk about a 3,000-mile, high-angle rocket, shot from one continent to another carrying an atomic bomb and so directed to be a precise weapon which would land exactly on a certain target such as a city.

"I say technically I don't think anybody in this world knows how to do such a thing, and I feel confident it will not be done for a very long period of time to come. I think we can leave that out of our thinking. I wish the American people would leave it out of their thinking."

Whether the idea was seriously on the minds of American people or not, it had occurred to German engineers during World War II. They had made preliminary designs for a long-range bomber which would be boosted into space by a rocket, then descend and skip off the atmosphere several times, coasting all the way to New York with its bomb load.

Ironically, at the very time Bush was urging Congress to forget missiles, von Braun and his team were languishing at Fort Bliss, Texas, making upper-atmosphere experiments with captured V-2s.

But with a nuclear monopoly, Congress was in no mood to finance development of long-range missiles for the Air Force, so nothing was done in these early years.

Then the short-lived nuclear monopoly came to an end. The Soviet Union exploded its first atomic bomb in 1949, just four years after the surrender of Japan ended World War II. President Truman ordered the United States to push development of the hydrogen bomb.

At the same time, the Russians were manufacturing improved V-2 rockets. In 1953, they started work on longer-range rockets, even though they still did not know when they would be able to make an atomic bomb small enough to be carried by a missile.

In the United States, the Air Force started work on its Atlas intercontinental missile in 1951, but the project moved slowly until 1954, when it became clear that the shrinkage of nuclear weapons made the intercontinental ballistic missile the weapon of the future.

The two atomic bombs dropped on Japan in World War II weighed some 10,000 pounds each and generated explosions equivalent to 20,000 tons of TNT, yet only a fraction of this weight was taken up by the explosive material itself. Both were fission weapons, which trigger their enormous energy release by bringing together a mass of uranium or plutonium so that the atoms split in an explosive chain reaction.

Hydrogen bombs, on the other hand, generate explosions by fusing atoms of heavy hydrogen. When this phenomenon was first uncovered, it was feared that such an uncontrolled explosion might destroy the whole world.

The United States, forging ahead of the Soviet Union in the arms race again, exploded its first hydrogen bomb in 1952. Though the device weighed some 60,000 pounds, it was soon apparent that a later version could be built that would be a fraction of the size of the first atomic bombs. This was the breakthrough that shot ICBM development to the top of national priorities.

Indeed, it was decided that it was not necessary to build the Atlas missile so large and powerful as had initially been thought. Two of its five engines were discarded to make the rocket simpler and more reliable. Even at that, Atlas was to be able to carry an H-bomb payload 250 times as powerful as the atomic bombs dropped in World War II.

The die for the early years of the space age was cast, forged in a contest for military supremacy between the world's two superpowers.

While the Soviet Union worked on its long-range missiles, a bitter struggle raged between the armed services in the United States for the leading role in missile development. Because the Atlas would not be ready until the late 1950s, planners turned toward intermediate-range missiles, which could be built sooner, to fill the gap. The Army claimed these were extensions of artillery, and therefore its responsibility, while the Air Force insisted they were strategic weapons belonging in its exclusive domain.

Finally, in 1956, the Defense Department issued firm guidelines, giving the Army responsibility for missiles of 200-miles' range or less, the Navy for ship-launched missiles, and the Air Force the rest.

Meanwhile, in the field of nonmilitary space science, the United States had announced plans to launch an instrumented scientific satellite as part of the International Geophysical Year, beginning in mid-1957.

The Administration wanted to keep space research removed from the military arena. It certainly did not want to increase the competition between Army and Air Force missilemen.

So the coveted assignment of launching the satellite—a beach-ball-sized sphere—went to the Naval Research Laboratory and a contractual team using a slender rocket called Vanguard.

The Vanguard had three stages—two rockets used in previous

tests to probe the upper atmosphere and a new third-stage rocket.

Understandably, the United States was more concerned about getting military missiles than it was about launching a satellite. Only a few technical people could foresee what was coming in space.

The United States was jolted in August 1957 when the Soviet Union announced that it had test-fired a multistage intercontinental missile. It was the "impossible" weapon Vannevar Bush had urged the country just 12 years earlier to forget.

As controversy over a potential "missile gap" boiled, little attention was paid to what the Russians were saying about using their rockets for space science. As far back as 1953, the president of the Soviet Academy of Sciences had told an international meeting in Vienna: "Science has reached a state where it is feasible to send a stratoplane to the moon, to create an artificial satellite of the earth."

After the United States announced plans to launch its Vanguard satellite during the International Geophysical Year, a Soviet scientist said that the Russians, too, had such plans, but that their satellite would be larger than Vanguard's. Several months before Sputnik was launched, the Soviet press even announced the broadcast frequency the satellite would use. No one in this country paid much attention to any of this. Leaders smugly assumed that a U.S. satellite would be first to circle the earth. The shock when Sputnik went up was intense. Its 184-pound weight, compared to our planned 21½-pound IGY satellite, seemed gigantic.

To some people, it was as intimidating as if the Russians had placed an atomic bomb in orbit. Though top officials in the Eisenhower Administration at first tried to dismiss the satellite as an insignificant stunt, its impact was not lost on the world or on the American public.

The Soviet Union had opened a new age as surely as the Wright brothers' first flight at Kitty Hawk, North Carolina, had given birth to aviation.

The worst for U.S. pride was yet to come. Before the excitement from the world's first satellite subsided, the Russians launched a second Sputnik weighing a hefty 1,100 pounds.

The most significant thing about Sputnik 2 was that it carried the dog Laika inside, and the Soviets monitored the animal's heartbeat and other vital functions as it circled the earth.

The Soviet Union had demonstrated great rocket power and the ability to launch heavy weights into space with this power. The presence of the dog inside the satellite showed clearly that the Russians were preparing to send men into orbit.

On December 6, a month after Sputnik 2, Vanguard was finally ready to go. As a nationwide television audience watched, the rocket blew up on the launch pad.

Shortly afterward, the U.S. Army missile team led by von Braun revived its satellite proposal, a scheme for using the Redstone missile tipped by a package of solid rockets to give a small satellite orbital velocity. At last they were given permission to go ahead.

On February 1, 1958, the Army team shot Explorer 1 into space with a 31-pound instrument package which discovered the Van Allen radiation belts that surround our planet, huge

Laika, the first living thing to orbit the earth. Unable to return, the dog died in space.

doughnut-shaped rings of magnetically trapped radiation from the sun. The achievement still stands as one of the more significant scientific discoveries of the space age. But at the time this was small consolation in view of what the Russians had accomplished.

The United States was now confronted by a challenge unlike any it had ever faced before. It was caught up in two races with the Soviet Union—one to bring missiles into full military capability, the other to catch up in exploiting space technology. We had fallen behind on both counts because of shortsightedness in the years just after World War II.

Not unexpectedly, the White House was besieged with recommendations on what to do. The Air Force Scientific Advisory Board, calling Sputnik and Russian missiles "a national emergency," recommended an early goal of landing on the moon. The American Rocket Society, composed of engineers in government, industry, and the colleges, had the same idea, and called for a national space program separated from the development of weapons.

The Army Ballistic Missile Agency proposed a shortcut for early development of a powerful new space launcher by clustering rockets already in existence. This was the concept which eventually led to the Saturn rockets.

The Army, the Air Force, and the Navy all put together man-in-space proposals, some of them based on ideas which had been in existence for years.

In mid-1958, the country began to get organized for its comeback. Congress created the National Aeronautics and Space Administration, giving it broad responsibility but leaving space activities directly related to defense to the Pentagon. NASA began operating on October 1, 1958.

Congress did not specify, however, whether manned spaceflight would be carried out by NASA or the Defense Department. The Air Force was anxious to get started with a manned space program. A month after NASA was organized, the White House ordered NASA to proceed with a manned satellite, later called Mercury. Basically, it was to learn whether man could tolerate weightlessness and function as a pilot in space.

Work began immediately. The agency pushed ahead, not only on development of the one-man spacecraft to carry a pilot into orbit atop the Atlas ICBM, but also on a 10-year plan of space exploration. When completed, this plan called for manned flights around the moon before 1970 and a landing on the moon in the early 1970s.

At the same time, the Army was given the go-ahead to develop the Saturn super-rocket. The shortcut the von Braun team had in mind was to cluster fuel tanks and rocket engines—with eight elongated Redstone-missile tanks around a larger Jupiter tank, and eight powerful engines at the bottom.

This produced a first-stage booster that could generate a takeoff thrust of 1.5 million pounds, far more than the Soviets had used to orbit even their largest Sputnik.

Long before the first Saturn 1 was ever assembled, however, the Army decided it had no military role for it. So the Saturn project and the von Braun team were transferred to NASA.

It was clear by now that the United States could not soon match the spectacular Soviet achievements in space.

In 1959, the Russians hit the moon with the Luna 2 probe and followed that by sending Luna 3 around the moon to get the first pictures of the hidden side of the moon.

Although the quality of the photographs was poor, they gave man a glimpse of a moonscape he had never seen before.

In 1960, the Soviets shattered their own weightlifting record with Sputniks 4 and 5. Both weighed more than 10,000 pounds.

Actually, these were prototypes of the Russians' first manned spacecraft. Sputnik 5 carried two dogs, Belka and Strelka, which landed after 18 orbits, becoming the first living things to go into orbit and return. There had been no way to recover Sputnik 2. The dog Laika had died in space.

Both the United States and the Soviets were moving rapidly toward manned flight in space. Though the United States still lagged far behind in rocket power, it hoped to regain some of its lost prestige by putting the first man in space.

The United States planned to conclude its preliminary tests

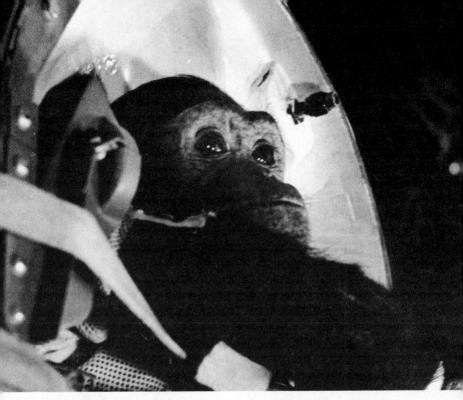

Enos, America's first living creature to orbit the earth. Unlike Laika, the chimpanzee returned from space.

of the cramped Mercury spacecraft with short spaceflights over the Atlantic, first with a chimpanzee aboard, then with an astronaut aboard on at least two flights. After that, a chimpanzee would be fired into orbit. Then Mercury would be ready to send Americans around the globe.

The suborbital spaceflights were to be boosted by the Army's Redstone; the orbital missions by the Air Force's Atlas, a rocket under development since 1951.

But before the first Mercury astronaut was launched even in suborbital flight, the Soviets launched Vostok 1 into orbit with Cosmonaut Yuri Gagarin. His spacecraft was 3 times as heavy as the Mercury capsule.

It was April 12, 1961, and to the world, the United States seemed as far behind as ever.

The following month, Navy Commander Alan B. Shepard, Jr., rode the Mercury spacecraft to an altitude of 116 miles and a speed of 5,180 miles per hour before splashing into the Atlantic 302 miles from what is now Cape Kennedy (then Cape Canaveral). It was a tremendous lift to U.S. hopes, even though Mercury seemed puny compared to Vostok.

Three of the six manned flights in the Mercury program ended hazardously. There was reason to wonder whether manned spacecraft would ever lead to anything practical.

Astronaut Virgil I. (Gus) Grissom, in the second suborbital flight, very nearly drowned when his Liberty Bell 7 suddenly began to sink in the Atlantic after he splashed down. The stubby, crewcut Air Force captain had ridden the spacecraft to an altitude of 118 miles and a distance of 303 miles from Cape Canaveral in an arcing shot that permitted him to experience weightlessness for five minutes as he went over the top.

As recovery helicopters dashed to pluck Liberty Bell 7 from the sea, the explosive bolts holding the spacecraft's hatch in place suddenly detonated. Seawater poured through the opening into the spacecraft cabin as Grissom struggled through it and bobbed to the surface.

In seconds, Grissom's space suit filled with water. He managed to keep himself afloat for nearly four minutes. Just as exhaustion overcame him, a helicopter arrived and dropped him a line with a rescue rig to slip under his arms.

Liberty Bell 7 filled with water and sank to the bottom of the ocean.

After that brush with near-tragedy, Mercury successfully flew in orbit with a chimpanzee named Enos and the United States prepared at last to put man in orbit.

The following February, John H. Glenn, Jr., rode his spacecraft Friendship 7 into orbit. The whole world followed Glenn's flight, impressed by his matter-of-fact manner and thrilled by his descriptions of the earth. The televised buildup to the flight and the drama of Glenn's launch showed an important difference between the American and Russian space efforts—one conducted in secrecy, the other publicly displayed to the whole world.

Then, as Glenn prepared for his return to earth at the end of his third orbit, the possibility of disaster loomed.

It began when engineers in the Mercury Control Center at Cape Canaveral saw a light glowing on a panel which told them that a clamp holding Friendship 7's heat shield in place had prematurely released. If that were the case, America's first man in orbit would be cremated as his capsule plunged toward earth, hitting the atmosphere at nearly 18,000 miles per hour and driving the temperature on the spaceship to several thousand degrees.

There seemed to be nothing Glenn or anyone on earth could

Alan B. Shepard, Jr., America's first man in space.

do. The one ray of hope was to keep the package of braking rockets—used to kick the spacecraft out of orbit and start it toward earth—attached to the capsule's heat shield. Normally, this rocket package was to be discarded after it had fired. If the heat shield really was loose, perhaps the spent rocket package would hold it in place.

Down Glenn plunged from orbit, his spacecraft turning into a meteor surrounded by a sheath of fiery gas that blacked out radio communication.

Mercifully, it turned out that the warning in the control room had been only a faulty electronic signal. The heat shield was secure; John Glenn was safe.

The package of braking rockets burned and disintegrated into flaming debris that flew past Glenn's window as he pierced the earth's atmosphere. He had not been told what controllers on the ground feared, but he had figured it out for himself.

Most of the world—unaccustomed to the language of spaceflight and unfamiliar with its intricacies—was unaware of the reentry drama until Glenn was safely on earth.

Three months later, however, the dangers of spaceflight were not so obscure.

After a three-orbit mission much like Glenn's, Astronaut Scott Carpenter found himself almost out of maneuvering fuel in Aurora 7. He was forced to drift aimlessly in flight for 77 minutes.

When Carpenter fired his braking rockets to start downward, he was three seconds late in triggering them. To make matters worse. the spacecraft was not properly oriented. As a result, he overshot his expected landing point by 250 miles, coming down 125 miles northeast of Puerto Rico.

It took rescuers three hours to reach him, and when they did, he was sitting on a life raft riding the waves beside Aurora 7.

Today. the spaceships used in Project Mercury are museum pieces. One who is accustomed now to the size and complexity of Apollo can scarcely look at the Mercury relics without feeling an overwhelming admiration for the men who flew them.

The Mercury cabin looks like a torture chamber. The pilot

was squeezed into a form-fitting couch, surrounded by controls, instruments, and life-support equipment, leaving him less freedom of movement than a fat man in a telephone booth. He was able to look outside through two small windows over his head or through a periscope.

In orbit, the Mercury spacecraft could do nothing to change its path of flight. It could only roll, pitch up and down, or yaw from side to side, using small control jets positioned around its base and its nose. Nor could the Mercury astronaut steer his capsule to a selected landing spot. His coming down in the immediate vicinity of recovery ships depended entirely on his firing the three braking rockets at precisely the right moment and having the spacecraft oriented properly when he did it.

The Mercury spacecraft was a crude beginner in the era of manned spaceflight. Nevertheless, it was a remarkable vehicle. The power of U.S. rockets dictated that it be small; the rush to get man into space meant that it had to be fashioned largely from existing technology.

Into a spacecraft which weighed about 1½ tons and measured 6 feet wide by 9 feet long, engineers had crammed 7 miles of wiring, dual control systems to be operated automatically or by the pilot, and a life-support system capable of keeping astronauts healthy if not completely comfortable.

In spite of the hair-raising endings of the Grissom, Glenn, and Carpenter missions, the effect of Project Mercury was to convince space engineers more than ever that they were ready to send men to the moon and to do it on the timetable that John Kennedy had proposed just after Alan Shepard's flight.

Six manned Mercury flights, four of them in orbit, showed that man could not only endure weightlessness, but could continue to function normally. They proved that pilots could easily withstand the forces of launch by powerful rockets and the fantastic decelerations when a spacecraft returns through the atmosphere.

Instead of disabling nausea and disorientation, the Mercury pilots found that their main medical problems were managing simple personal hygiene and recovering from a condition called

The First Men in Space

U.S. Mercury Program

Mercury 3 / *May 5, 1961*
Suborbital

Alan B. Shepard, Jr.

Mercury 4 / *July 21, 1961*
Suborbital

Virgil I. Grissom

Mercury 6 / *Feb. 20, 1962*
3 Orbits

John H. Glenn, Jr.

Mercury 7 / *May 24, 1962*
3 Orbits

M. Scott Carpenter

Mercury 8 / *Oct. 3, 1962*
6 Orbits

Walter M. Schirra, Jr.

Mercury 9 / *May 15, 1963*
22 Orbits

L. Gordon Cooper, Jr.

The First Men in Space

U.S.S.R. Vostok Program

Vostok 1 / *April 12, 1961*
1 Orbit

Yuri A. Gagarin

Vostok 2 / *Aug. 6, 1961*
17 Orbits

Gherman S. Titov

Vostok 3 / *Aug. 11, 1962*
64 Orbits

Andrian G. Nikolayev

Vostok 4 / *Aug. 12, 1962*
48 Orbits

Pavel R. Popovitch

Vostok 5 / *June 14, 1963*
81 Orbits

Valery F. Bykovsky

Vostok 6 / *June 16, 1963*
48 Orbits

Valentina V. Tereshkova

"orthostatic hypotension." This is caused by a pooling of blood in the legs after flight, producing brief dizziness. The same thing happens to medical patients confined to bed for prolonged periods.

Recovery was always rapid, within a matter of hours, and physicians found that they could control the condition quite successfully by having astronauts exercise with a stretchable cord which they pulled with their hands and feet.

In the six manned flights, Mercury evolved rapidly from a satellite with a man in it into something approaching a true spacecraft.

The first astronauts to fly in Mercury were almost comparable, as passengers, to the chimpanzee which had ridden in test flights. But the astronauts quickly started to demonstrate that they could give the automatic equipment a helping hand.

For example, when a control jet stuck during Glenn's historic mission, the Marine colonel took control of Friendship 7 and handled it as deftly as he had the jet fighters he tested before he was selected to be one of America's original seven space pilots.

Glenn's flight actually fulfilled the original objectives of the Mercury program. The final two flights gave man increasing control over the capsule.

Walter M. Schirra, Jr., on May 3, 1962, took his Sigma 7 Mercury ship on a 6-orbit trip of such perfection that it is still at the top of the list of those labeled "textbook" ventures of man in space. It set the stage for a Mercury finale far more ambitious than anyone had expected when the program began—a 22-orbit marathon lasting for 34 hours. It was undertaken a year later by L. Gordon Cooper, the youngest of the original astronauts.

Cooper startled laymen and touched off spirited arguments among scientists with his keen observations of earth from space. Some said that it was physically impossible for Cooper to have seen the things he reported spotting from an altitude of more than 100 miles—smoke coming from chimneys, wakes behind boats, and smoke from moving trains.

Subsequent flights and photography of the earth from Project

Gemini spacecraft showed that Cooper was right. Adding to man's attributes as part of a space-exploration system, Cooper demonstrated the amazing ability of man's unaided eyes to observe the earth, as through a clear telescope, from an orbiting spacecraft.

At the end of a full day in space, Cooper became the first American astronaut to sign off his radio link with the ground, leave his spacecraft to itself, and go to sleep. Previously, he had managed to get a short nap while still on the launch pad with his Atlas rocket being fueled beneath him. So flight controllers on earth were not surprised that the laconic Air Force pilot was able to doze in orbit.

However, he found staying asleep in his capsule to be difficult. As he dozed, his weightless arms floated away from his body, waking him and making him fearful that he would accidentally hit a critical switch on the control panel in front of him. Finally, he was able partially to control the problem by hooking his thumbs under the shoulder harness of his space suit.

As Cooper's Faith 7 parachuted into the Atlantic, the United States had accumulated 53 hours and 55 minutes of manned spaceflight, covering a distance of nearly 901,000 miles. Only four years, four months, and four days had gone by since the government selected the McDonnell Company to build the first manned spacecraft. It was highly encouraging.

Once the United States began making its Mercury orbital flights, it stole the thunder from the Soviet space ventures throughout most of 1962.

In midsummer, the Soviet Union added a new dimension to the race by launching large Vostok spacecraft on successive days.

Vostok 3, piloted by Cosmonaut Andrian Nikolayev, went up on August 11. The following day Pavel Popovitch was launched in Vostok 4 with such accuracy that the vehicles passed within a reported 3.1 miles of each other in orbit.

A month after the United States concluded Project Mercury with Cooper's flight in May 1963, Vostok 5 and Vostok 6 made another dual flight for the Soviet Union. They passed even closer together than Vostoks 3 and 4 had the previous summer. Vostok 5 established another spaceflight endurance record by circling the earth 81 times before landing. The longest of the Mercury flights had amassed only 34 orbits, and all of them combined, 46.

But the "first" which brought world attention to the second double-header of the Vostok program was the fact that Vostok 6 was piloted by a woman, Valentina Tereshkova.

It seemed clear that the Soviets were extremely close to carrying out a rendezvous operation to join or dock two craft in space. This would be a crucial step on the way to the moon, the one the U.S. Gemini program was designed to perfect. But Gemini was nearly two years away. Compared to the impressive flights of Vostoks 1 through 6 even Cooper's marathon Mercury mission seemed behind the times.

The United States, nearly six years after the first Sputnik, still was not catching up with the Russians in the more complicated and impressive aspects of space exploration.

CHAPTER TEN

The Next Big Step: Gemini

Before the United States could launch its first astronauts in the new two-man Gemini spacecraft to start closing the gap, the Soviets in 1964 won another heat in the race by orbiting three cosmonauts in a new spacecraft called Voskhod 1. The ship circled the earth 16 times before coming down. It weighed about 16,000 pounds, several times the size and weight of any satellite that the United States was able to launch at that time.

Five months later another Voskhod was sent into orbit. To the amazement of mankind, Cosmonaut Alexei Leonov crawled through an airlock and left the craft for a "walk" in space. He floated beside the spacecraft for 10 minutes, a human satellite in orbit around the earth.

It was another achievement of historic importance. If man is to make himself useful in space, he cannot be confined to the inside of his spacecraft. In the future he will be called upon to make repairs on orbiting satellites, to help refuel spaceships bound for the planets, or to work outside on the construction of space stations or orbiting telescopes.

Leonov, tethered to the spacecraft, only floated along with it, but he had surmounted another barrier which man could scarcely have hoped to surmount only a few years before.

Following the pattern established early in its manned flight program, Russia then removed its accomplishments from public view. In two long strides it had accomplished what it wanted from Voskhod and flew it no more. It would be well over a year before another cosmonaut circled the earth, and in that year the United States would draw even with the Soviets for the first time.

Immediately after Sputnik, there had been little the United States could do to overcome the Soviet lead because it did not then have the rocket power needed. But while American scientists were developing boosters to approach the weightlifting capability of the Russians, the United States was able to start matching them step by step in many other areas. This was possible because we had the advantages of new materials, miniature electronics, and other engineering know-how which allowed us to accomplish a great deal even with space vehicles smaller than those of the Russians.

More important, Americans were developing the basic techniques necessary to get to the moon and back. We were also in the midst of an unmanned moon-exploration program, using remote-controlled, TV-equipped devices which were producing more specific knowledge about the lunar surface than scientists had gathered in all previous history. We had learned that we

---

The
First Men
in Space

U.S.S.R.
Voskhod Program

Voskhod 1 / *Oct. 12, 1964*   16 Orbits

Vladimir M. Komarov

Konstantin P. Feoktisto

could safely set down our moon-landing vehicle on the lunar surface.

The two-man Gemini spacecraft already was under construction when Project Mercury came to an end. Gemini was to be used to perfect the basic techniques the United States would need to get to the moon.

Comparing the new Gemini to Mercury was like comparing a modern-day jetliner to the lumbering airliners of the 1940s.

Mercury gave Gemini its basic shape—the unusual design of a spacecraft which comes down for a landing blunt end first. This is a good example of the original kind of thinking that was essential in the space age.

Back in 1952, when space travel was just a dream, a brilliant aeronautical engineer named H. Julian Allen showed that this was the best way for a vehicle plunging down from space to survive its searing encounter with the atmosphere. It was a radical departure from the seemingly more sensible approach of diving in with a streamlined nose first.

Allen's achievement solved one of the technical problems which had made U.S. officials pessimistic about the feasibility of the ICBM. They had not been able to figure out how to get atomic warheads down through the atmosphere without their being destroyed by the heat. Allen's discovery, in solving that

Voskhod 2 / *March 18, 1965* 17 Orbits

Boris G. Yegorov   Aleksei A. Leonov   Pavel I. Belyayev

problem, also showed what shape was needed for the Mercury and Gemini spacecraft.

In 10 manned space ventures in 1965 and 1966, Gemini astronauts became the first men to change the orbit of their spaceship. They made the world's first rendezvous and docking in orbit. They set new records for altitude and endurance.

These records were not too important in themselves, but in setting them, American astronauts passed crucial milestones on the way to the moon. They showed that the technique we had chosen for getting men to the moon and back would indeed work.

Rendezvous and docking probably are the two most important maneuvers in manned spaceflight. America's plan for getting men to the moon and back was based on this ability to bring two vehicles together in space and to attach them to each other. Without the ability to rendezvous and dock, the only way to go to the moon would be to build a gigantic rocket which could fly there directly from earth, and then take off again for the voyage home.

The United States once had a plan for such a rocket, called Nova. It would have dwarfed the 364-foot tall Saturn 5. Its first stage would have produced 12 to 15 million pounds of thrust, an unbelievable amount of power.

The smaller Saturn 5, lifting off the earth with a thrust of 7.5 million pounds, has the equivalent of 160 million horsepower, about double the power that would be produced if all the rivers and streams in North America were channeled through turbines. Even this is not enough power to fly to the moon without rendezvous.

Shortly after the moon landing goal was established, space experts had decided that a rendezvous would be necessary. This could be done in several ways.

The most obvious of these would be to launch two huge rockets into earth orbit. One would carry a manned spacecraft while the other would carry fuel. Bringing the two together in space would permit fuel to be transferred from the tanker into the rocket bound for the moon. The latter, with a new

Cosmonaut Aleksei Leonov as he floats in space—the first human being to do so. The Cyrillic CCCP on his helmet are the Russian letters for U.S.S.R.

source of power, then would blast out of earth orbit carrying its passengers on their way.

The development of the Soviet Union's manned space program from the beginning indicated that they planned some such scheme for flying to the moon, although they have never said as much. In fact, their statements about plans have been so ambiguous that we have been left in the dark about what they really have in mind.

The United States in 1962 decided to approach the moon landing by using rendezvous in a different way. We settled on a plan to launch two space vehicles attached together on earth and send them into orbit around the moon. We decided that only a lightweight landing craft, or taxi, should go down to the moon's surface. It would carry two crew members and leave a third orbiting the moon in the command ship.

To return home, the taxi is launched back into moon orbit to rendezvous with the mother ship. The vehicles dock and the two explorers crawl from the taxi back into the command ship for the return flight. This approach permits the landing to be carried out without an immense rocket such as Nova and without the need to refuel in earth orbit. The lightweight taxi does not require much rocket power to take off from the moon.

If the entire Apollo vehicle landed, it would have to carry the heavy heat shield which protects the spacecraft as it returns to earth through our atmosphere and other heavy equipment of no use in actual landing on the moon, plus the extra fuel necessary to rocket all this added weight back to earth against the pull of the moon's gravity.

The ability to rendezvous in moon orbit makes it possible to land and take off from the lunar surface with a minimum of weight, and, therefore, a minimum amount of rocket power.

But this is getting ahead of the story. At first, most officials in NASA had focused on development of the huge Nova rocket. What troubled them, though, was the tremendous cost of building such a rocket. Also, they doubted that it could be completed in time to make the first moon landing in the 1960s. These thoughts brought them to the view that a rendezvous of some kind would be necessary.

Next, they turned to the earth-orbit rendezvous and refueling approach. But a small group of engineers at NASA's Langley Research Center in Virginia questioned this approach, too. They put together still another proposal. This was the lunar-orbit rendezvous plan. For a year, a persistent young mathematician-engineer named John Houbolt tried to get a full hearing for this alternative scheme.

Most of his superiors in the space agency who bothered to listen were at first set against it. They simply did not like the idea of trying the complicated rendezvous and docking so far away from earth.

Finally, Houbolt was able to get a full review for the concept.

When it was thoroughly studied, the top leadership in NASA headquarters agreed that this was indeed the best way. It offered a chance to get to the moon sooner, at less cost, and with as much safety as the earth-orbital refueling method.

Project Gemini—named after the twin Gemini stars because two astronauts were to fly the spacecraft—was created to perfect rendezvous and docking. Coming between Project Mercury and Project Apollo, Gemini allowed pilots to gather much experience, in effect learning how to make moon flights long before the Apollo spaceship itself was ready for flight. All this was done with a spacecraft that weighed only about 4 tons, as compared to 8 tons for the newest Soviet manned spacecraft.

Although it was small, Gemini was sophisticated in many ways. For instance, instead of using storage batteries to provide electrical power, it generated its own electricity with advanced devices called fuel cells.

Gemini derived the great maneuverability necessary for rendezvous from 32 small rocket thrusters fixed in different positions over its exterior. When fired properly, they could move the spacecraft in any direction. Returning to earth at the end of their orbital missions, Gemini pilots—unlike those of Mercury—could maneuver their spacecraft over a wide area to bring them down near recovery ships.

Normally, the Gemini spacecraft guided themselves down from orbit, their on-board computers rapidly calculating positions in relation to targets and sending commands to control thrusters to alter descent. The same remarkable computers told astronauts what maneuvers to make in order to rendezvous with orbiting targets.

In most rendezvous flights, targets were Agena rockets launched into orbit from Cape Kennedy before the Gemini pilots took off.

The Agena, for Gemini exercises, was equipped with a docking collar on the opposite end of the rocket from its 16,000-pound thrust engine. To dock, the astronauts had to learn to put the nose of the Gemini into the docking collar. Once joined, the spacecraft and rocket were held rigidly by the collar. Astronauts were then able to fire the Agena engine and boost their space-craft to altitudes unachievable with Gemini's own propulsion system.

To rendezvous, radar in the nose of the spacecraft would spot the target and the computer would calculate distance and the rate of speed at which the spacecraft was approaching or reced-ing from the target. The same information was fed to the com-puter from tracking stations following both the Gemini and Agena on earth.

With such pinpoint data, the spacecraft computer could cal-culate how much and in what direction the astronauts should fire their thrusters to close in on the target.

Our astronauts discovered that rendezvous in space is not a matter of simply finding the target and heading straight for it. The laws of orbital mechanics play strange tricks.

Consider a spacecraft attempting to catch up with a target several miles away and straight ahead. In a vehicle on earth, you accelerate to catch up. In space, however, when a vehicle accelerates, it goes into a higher orbit. It is, therefore, traveling in a larger circle around the earth. Because it is traveling farther, it falls behind the target instead of catching up.

The opposite is also true. So to catch up and rendezvous with a target, astronauts fire thrusters to slow the spacecraft. This puts them into a lower and shorter orbit.

Because the spacecraft is now traveling a shorter distance around the earth, it is taking the inside track. It passes beneath the target and then is elevated to rendezvous with it.

In Gemini's initial manned flight, Astronauts Virgil I. (Gus) Grissom and Edward H. White II became the first pilots to change the shape of their orbit. They did not rendezvous. No target was launched ahead of them. Their task was simply to check out the new spacecraft's ability to make the rendezvous maneuver.

It was one of the United States' first significant manned flight accomplishments that the Russians hadn't already demonstrated.

New feats to bring the score in favor of the United States came routinely as the Gemini program progressed. By the time the project was over, the United States had made 16 manned flights to 8 for the Soviet Union. Americans had accumulated nearly 1,900 man hours in space as compared with 507 for Russia. Gemini produced a collection of 2,400 photographs of earth, conducted 19 scientific experiments, and carried out 15 cooperative tasks with the Department of Defense.

Gemini demonstrated 10 different rendezvous techniques, including rendezvous on a spacecraft's first orbit.

This latter was a rare demonstration of precision, for it required the spacecraft to be launched from earth within an exact two-second interval in order to start out near enough to the target to make quick rendezvous possible.

The historic first rendezvous in space came as Gemini 6 and Gemini 7, piloted by Astronauts Walter M. Schirra, Jr., and Tom P. Stafford, caught up with the Gemini 6 in 5 hours and 18 minutes. Gemini 6, with Astronauts Frank Borman and James A. Lovell, Jr., aboard, was in the midst of a two-week marathon flight to remove the last doubts about whether man could endure weightlessness for long periods without ill effects.

The two spacecraft had no attachments to permit them actually to link up. They did move within inches of each other, so close that the crews photographed one another peering through their windows.

The first space docking came on the Gemini 8 flight. However, as it worked out, before Astronauts Neil A. Armstrong and David R. Scott had a chance to fire up the Agena rocket engine, a control thruster on Gemini became stuck, sending the docked vehicles into a wild, uncontrolled roll.

Armstrong disengaged from the Agena, backed away, and put his reentry control system into emergency use to bring the spacecraft out of its roll. A short time later, he and Scott made an emergency landing in the Pacific, the first time a U.S. spaceflight was cut short by danger in orbit.

Subsequently, both Gemini 10 and Gemini 11 docked with Agena rockets and used them to climb far higher than man had ever gone before. Gemini 10 reached an altitude of 468 miles, and two months later Gemini 11, with Charles Conrad, Jr., and

Richard F. Gordon, Jr., went to an altitude of 850 miles.

Astronauts' attempts to work outside the Gemini spacecraft gave flight planners a far deeper respect for the difficulties of working in weightlessness. With no gravity and nothing to sit or stand on, the astronauts tumbled and rolled.

Astronaut White, in Gemini 4, made the first space walk by a U.S. astronaut just three months after Leonov had floated for 20 minutes about 100 miles above the earth, tethered by a nylon leash to the spacecraft.

Astronaut Eugene A. Cernan made the first attempt to perform specific tasks. He went outside Gemini 9 and worked his way to the rear of the spacecraft where a maneuvering unit, equipped with small thrusters, had been stored during launch. He was supposed to strap the outfit on his back and use it to move about outside the orbiting spacecraft. Cernan found it an exhausting task just to get the device on his back. He sweated so profusely that the faceplate of his space helmet fogged. He was ordered back into the cockpit.

Astronaut Michael Collins had somewhat more luck on Gemini 10, but he, too, found that every movement in his pressurized space suit—with no gravity to anchor him—was strenuous. Finally, he became entangled in the line feeding oxygen to him. He had to have help from Astronaut John W. Young to get back inside.

On Gemini 11, Astronaut Gordon admitted that he was "pooped" only 6 minutes after he opened his hatch. His heart raced to 180 beats per minute. He managed to stay out in space 44 minutes before getting back into the spacecraft and calling off several of his planned experiments.

Not until Gemini 12, the final flight of the program, did officials feel they were really making progress in learning how to conduct this "extravehicular activity" or EVA.

Astronaut Edwin E. Aldrin, Jr., spent many days preparing for his space walk by working underwater in his pressurized space suit.

Engineers devised hand grips and other devices to help Aldrin hold himself to the spacecraft while he took pictures, practiced

Astronaut Edward H. White II floating in space—the first American to do so.

Gemini 3 / *March 23, 1965*
3 Orbits

Virgil I. Grissom

The First Men in Space

U.S. Gemini Program

John W. Young

Gemini 4 / *June 3, 1965*
62 Orbits

James A. McDivitt

Edward H. White, II

Gemini 5 / *Aug. 21, 1965*
120 Orbits

L. Gordon Cooper, Jr.

Charles Conrad, Jr.

Gemini 7 / *Dec. 4, 196*
206 Orbits

Frank Borman

James A. Lovell, Jr.

Gemini 6a / *Dec. 15, 1965*
6 Orbits

Walter M. Schirra, Jr.

Tom P. Stafford

Gemini 8 / *March 16, 1966*
6.5 Orbits

Neil A. Armstrong

David R. Scott

Gemini 9a / *June 3, 1966*
45 Orbits

Tom P. Stafford

Eugene A. Cernan

Gemini 10 / *July 18, 1966*
43 Orbits

John W. Young

Michael Collins

Gemini 11 / *Sept. 12, 1966*
44 Orbits

Charles Conrad, Jr.

Richard F. Gordon, Jr.

Gemini 12 / *Nov. 11, 1966*
59 Orbits

James A. Lovell, Jr.

Edwin E. Aldrin, Jr.

tightening bolts, cleaned the Gemini windows, and did other tasks. He stayed outside for 2 hours and 20 minutes. Before the flight ended, he worked two more periods standing in his seat with the hatch open. Altogether he worked nearly 6 hours with the spacecraft open.

At last engineers felt they had learned to appreciate man's limited capacity to work outside an orbiting spacecraft. They immediately began taking a more conservative approach toward the first experiments on the surface of the moon, planning less strenuous tasks than heretofore conceived for the astronaut-explorers.

Project Gemini was over. A program intended simply to help prepare the way for Apollo had given the United States great new prestige in manned spaceflight in the eyes of the world.

Before and during this time, there was another important series of events taking place in the race for the moon, quite apart from the ventures of the astronauts. These were carried on by robot devices sent out as moon scouts by both the United States and Russia in preparation for manned landings.

Russia jumped ahead in that race, too, when its Luna 3 probe looped around the moon and sent back pictures in 1959.

The situation in this race was comparable to what happened in manned spaceflight. The United States started late. The Soviet Union reaped worldwide propaganda benefits from taking new steps first. It not only made the first photographs of the moon with an unmanned spacecraft but also actually hit the moon first. Lastly, it achieved the first gentle landing that put functioning scientific instruments on the surface to transmit information back to earth.

Notwithstanding, it was the United States which amassed the greatest new store of information. Repeating unmanned probes several times, the United States gave mankind a picture of the moon which could not be improved upon until men went there themselves.

Between 1964 and 1968, the United States collected more than 100,000 pictures of the moon. These were from 1 to 10 million times more detailed than the best pictures taken through

A Ranger spacecraft, one of our early unmanned vehicles to scout the surface of the moon in preparation for manned landings. Ranger relayed photographs of the moon and dropped instruments to measure lunar quakes.

telescopes from earth. Instead of objects the size of the Pentagon, some of these new pictures showed particles only fractions of an inch across.

The United States sent three different kinds of picture-taking spacecraft to scout the moon. Their job was to report on places smooth enough for a landing and on the firmness of the surface. The robots were called Rangers, Surveyors, and Lunar Orbiters.

The Rangers were designed to fly straight into the moon, taking pictures as they approached, down to the last split second before destroying themselves by crashing into the surface at several thousand miles per hour.

Surveyors, on the other hand, were "soft landers"—contraptions with spindly legs and rocket engines which fired downward as they approached the moon, lowering them to an easy landing.

Surveyors were to show scientists close-up pictures of tiny moon-surface particles as well as broad panoramas of the lunar landscape.

The third series of vehicles was to orbit the moon, inspecting a belt along its equator to examine sites where man might best land.

After partially successful flights for test purposes with Rangers 1 and 2, the United States had four straight failures attempting to get the first close-up views of the moon's surface. Ranger 3 was given too much thrust and shot past the moon. Number 4 crashed on the back side of the moon without sending back a single photo. Ranger 5 was another one that missed the moon altogether.

After a congressional investigation, some sharp criticism of project management, a review of the entire effort, and a delay of more than a year, another attempt was made.

Ranger 6 flew like a dream, on a perfect course. The whole U.S. space establishment waited breathlessly to see the first pictures on television. As the craft approached the moon with its six cameras pointing at the surface, a radio command was sent from the Jet Propulsion Laboratory at Pasadena, California, to turn on the cameras.

Nothing happened. Ranger 6 hit on target, but took not a single picture.

After this, the Rangers began to work. In 17 minutes before it crashed into a smooth area of the moon known as the Sea of Clouds, Ranger 7 sent back 4,300 photographs. Ranger 8 added 7,137 more before it hit the Sea of Tranquillity. Ranger 9 concluded the program by taking 5,814 additional pictures as it crashed into a crater called Alphonsus.

The Soviets, after first hitting the moon with a probe and

photographing its hidden side in 1959, ran into serious difficulties with unmanned lunar probes. Its Luna 4 missed by 5,000 miles in 1963. Attempting to make the first soft landing on the moon's surface, Luna 5 crashed in May 1965. Luna 6 missed by 100,000 miles.

Lunas 7 and 8 both hit the moon, but crashed instead of landing softly as had been intended.

As the Russians raced to make the first controlled landing on the moon, the United States prepared to launch its first Surveyor.

Russia won. After five straight failures, the Soviet Union put its Luna 9 on the surface of the moon in workable condition on January 31, 1966. For three days, Luna transmitted pictures back to earth, showing the surface of the moon from a few inches away.

These pictures destroyed the theory held by some respected scientists that the moon was covered by a deep layer of powdery dust which would swallow up manned spacecraft when they landed.

Now came the time for the U.S. soft-landing robot. In one of the most dramatic accomplishments of the U.S. space program to that moment, Surveyor 1 settled gently to the moon's surface on June 2, 1966.

As planned, its rocket engine slowed the vehicle to a near stop just 13 feet above the surface, then shut off. Surveyor dropped with a bounce, and 35 minutes later sent back a picture of one of its own footpads, planted firmly in soil that looked like a plowed field.

That virtually removed any doubt that man could safely land on the moon. Before lunar night came, the spacecraft sent back 10,338 pictures. They showed particles of moon soil clinging to Surveyor's feet, panoramic views of the landscape, the setting sun, even the device's own shadow as the sun sank toward the horizon.

Incredibly, Surveyor 1 survived the cold, two-week long lunar night and operated its cameras again on its second moon day.

Photographic work was stopped after that. Surveyor 1 had

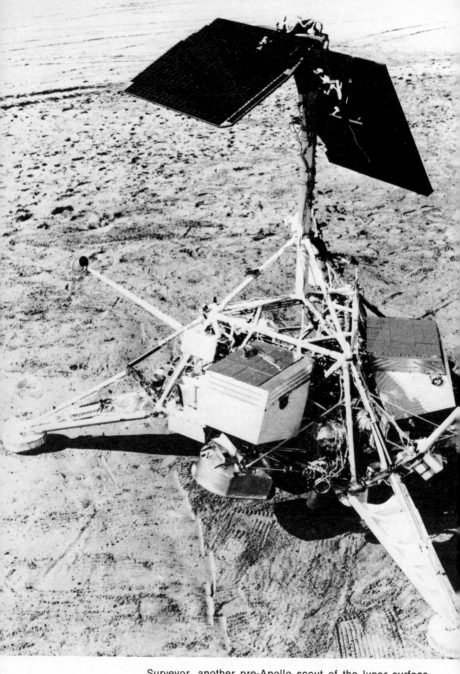

Surveyor, another pre-Apollo scout of the lunar surface.

Surveyor, after successfully making a soft landing on the moon, transmits this photograph of itself, indicating that the lunar surface could support the weight of man and his transport vehicle.

snapped pictures of everything in sight. It continued, however, to respond to signals sent from earth for eight months.

In seven landing attempts altogether, Surveyors succeeded five times. They proved that the moon's surface would support a manned landing vehicle.

Surveyor 3, equipped with a small, scooplike device commanded by radio signal from earth, dug into the surface, finding it solid and somewhat sticky, like wet beach sand. With the camera watching the scoop at work, the device picked up some objects only to have them crumble. Others were obviously rocks, for they refused to break even when the jaws of the scoop squeezed them with a force of more than 100 pounds per square inch.

If that was not enough, Surveyor 5 performed a chemical experiment on the moon's surface material, finding it to be basaltic rock. Such rocks are common on earth and are of volcanic origin.

Scientists made it possible to get some early insight into the chemical nature of the moon by equipping the Surveyor with a small container of radioactive material which the spacecraft lowered to the surface on a string. Such material emits particles of radiation. Scientists were able to make their identification of basaltic rock from the way these particles bounced back into delicate sensors.

At the same time the Surveyors were making these impressive tests, Lunar Orbiters were examining the scene from above. They dipped within 28 miles of the surface as they circled the moon.

Both the Rangers and Surveyors were a part of the country's space-exploration plans even before the moon landing goal was established. The Lunar Orbiter program was added after the moon race began, and was given the specific role of examining potential manned landing sites from numerous angles and under varying conditions of light.

The landing sites for the early exploration of the moon have to be in a narrow belt along the equator on the side of the moon facing earth. Here is the reason: As a safety precaution,

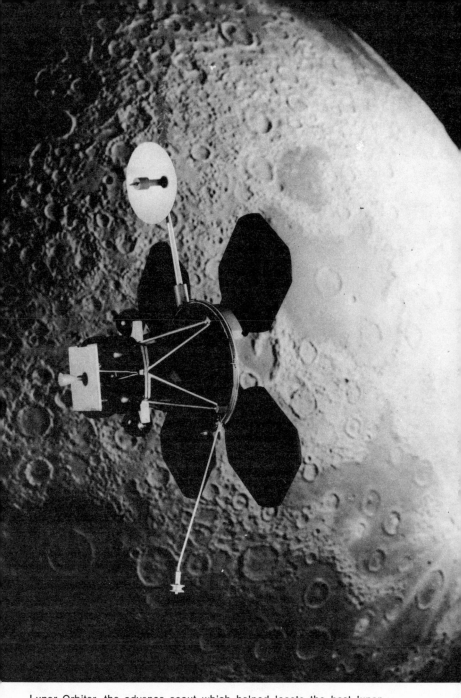

Lunar Orbiter, the advance scout which helped locate the best lunar landing sites for our astronauts.

astronauts fly to the moon on a path that will automatically bring them back to earth if they decide not to go into orbit around the moon or are unable to do so.

To follow this path means that, when the spacecraft does go into orbit, it must travel around the moon's equator. Such an orbit does not require as much fuel for the landing vehicle to descend to a site beneath the path of the mother ship as would be needed if the course were over the poles.

The first three Lunar Orbiters covered this area so well that it was possible for the last two to concentrate on other scientifically interesting areas. By the time the five Orbiter flights were completed, 99 percent of the moon's front side had been mapped in great detail, and most of the hidden side had been photographed clearly for the first time.

From the photographs of the Apollo landing zone, planners were able to select five sites which were smooth and uncratered enough for manned landings.

While the Russians remained singularly silent during this period, the United States was getting ready for the giant stride to its greatest undertaking of all—Project Apollo.

CHAPTER ELEVEN

The Winning Project: Apollo

The success of Project Gemini, our second generation of manned spaceflight, raised hopes that the United States might make it to the moon by the middle of 1968, leaving the Soviet Union well behind. The stage was set for Project Apollo, our third generation, to land astronauts on the moon and return them safely to earth. Apollo was to bring victory to the United States in the race against the Soviet Union.

However, the race by no means was over. There was no reason to believe that the Russians were ready to concede defeat. Rumors kept cropping up that they were preparing another space spectacular in an attempt to snatch the prize from the United States at the very last moment.

The Russians continued sending unmanned vehicles to the moon. They also kept launching Cosmos satellites regularly, never disclosing whether these were of a military nature or whether they were unmanned tests of a new spacecraft which might later carry Soviet cosmonauts to the moon.

If the Russians were unable to make a manned landing in time, according to one rumor cabled from Moscow, they would, as a last resort, try to make an unmanned landing with a robot which would return with the first sample of the moon's surface.

This would be intended to take some of the bloom off of the triumph of the expected U.S. manned landing.

NASA officials were mindful of the possibility of what they called "a quick Soviet snatch" of some moon samples. If anything, rumors of this kind simply spurred U.S. space planners on toward the big prize—the manned landing. And the prize was now in sight.

Then a terrible accident occurred. Fire broke out in an Apollo 1 spacecraft on January 27, 1967, as Astronauts Virgil Grissom, Edward White, and Roger Chaffee sat inside the ship, going through a mock launch practice. They were high atop a Saturn 1B rocket, sealed in their three-man spacecraft just as though they were really being launched. The cabin was filled with pure oxygen. In seconds, the fire turned the compartment into a furnace. The astronauts never had a chance to escape.

America's race for the moon came to a shuddering halt. After 14 orbital flights without so much as a cut finger, disaster had struck where it was least expected—on earth.

Spaceflight is too new and too dangerous for an accident not to happen sometime. But no one, least of all the people involved, expected it to come this way, in a training session on top of a rocket that was not even fueled.

It took expert investigators weeks to find the probable cause. They sorted out the wreckage of the ill-fated Apollo piece by piece, meticulously reconstructing the course the flames had taken in engulfing the cabin. They listened repeatedly to the last frantic words of the astronauts, hoping that these final radio transmissions would give some clue. Finally, their detective work uncovered the probable cause.

The insulation on an electrical wire had been scraped away by the opening and closing of a small door. A spark had jumped from the exposed wire. The pure oxygen force-drafted flames in the cockpit into an inferno. There was no single individual to blame, no specific, tragic mistake to pinpoint.

Top NASA officials admitted before a congressional investigation that they had become overconfident. They had not recognized how dangerous it was to have the spacecraft pressurized with pure oxygen and filled with materials that could ignite.

In the aftermath of the fire, some 5,000 engineering changes were ordered on Apollo, most of them for fireproofing both the command vehicle and the lunar taxi. Every scrap of flammable material was removed. The astronauts even got new space suits, made of glass-fiber material that will not burn under the most severe circumstances.

At the same time, the Apollo cabin was equipped with a new quick-opening hatch. The hatch of the earlier Apollo had been designed to open inward to avoid accidental opening in space. Because the spacecraft is pressurized and space is a vacuum, the hatch was designed this way so it would be held securely in place by the pressure in the cabin.

When the fire broke out, the rising pressure in the cabin held the door so firmly in place that tons of force would have been necessary to move it. The flames raced through so quickly that it did not matter which way the hatch opened. Even under normal conditions, it took 90 seconds to open the hatch. In less than that time, all three astronauts were unconscious or dead.

The quick-opening hatch opened outward. Great precautions were taken to avoid a chance of its opening accidentally in space.

At the same time, the environmental system was changed. Instead of using pure oxygen, Apollo was modified to use a combination of oxygen and nitrogen during the time it is pressurized on earth before launch. The mixture is more nearly like the air we breathe. If a spark did ignite something in the cabin, there would not be a flash fire like the one that roared through previously.

To keep from having to redesign the spacecraft's breathing system completely, engineers decided to use the mixed-gas atmosphere on earth and switch gradually to pure oxygen as Apollo climbed into space. The pure oxygen atmosphere had been chosen for Apollo because it had been used with great success in both the Mercury and Gemini programs. A spacecraft using pure oxygen does not have to be as highly pressurized as does one using a nitrogen-oxygen mixture. Thus, spacecraft design is simpler for such a system.

The Apollo fire changed the outlook of the moon race. It gave critics a wide-open chance to find fault with the space race and the cost of the moon program. They used the incident to put forth new arguments for exploring space with instruments rather than with men. Despite NASA's admission that it had been lulled into overconfidence by the string of successes in the Gemini program, there was little, if any, evidence to prove that the accident had been caused by the demanding timetable for carrying out the first manned landing on the moon.

While NASA and its contractors were deciding what to do to restore public confidence, Russia ended its long silence about manned spaceflight.

On April 22, less than three months after the Apollo tragedy, the Soviet Union launched a new spacecraft called Soyuz 1, piloted by Colonel Vladimir Komarov. It seemed that the gains the United States had made during Project Gemini might suddenly be surpassed as the Soviet Union entered the third phase of its own manned space-exploration program.

But the first flight in the new Soviet program ended in tragedy, too. After 18 orbits, Komarov plunged to earth and died. The lines of the spacecraft's landing parachute tangled so that it did not open enough to prevent a fatally rapid plunge to the ground.

Veteran observers of the Soviet Union's space program believed that more was involved in the accident than parachute failure. Some suspected that the spacecraft, after serious control problems in orbit, was making an emergency descent, probably out of control. This conclusion was based on the fact that Soyuz 1 did not start its reentry on the sixteenth or seventeenth orbits, when it would have been lined up with the normal landing area for Soviet manned space vehicles.

Dr. Charles Sheldon of the U.S. Library of Congress, one of the leading American experts on the Soviet space program, said:

"To put up one man for one day could not have been consistent with the rumors encouraged in Moscow that this would

Evolution of U.S. Spacecraft

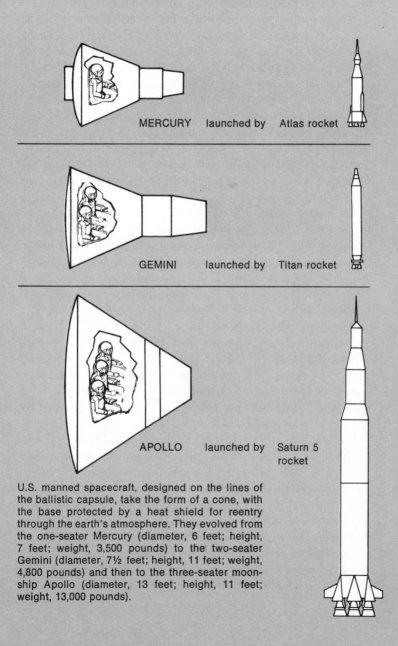

MERCURY   launched by   Atlas rocket

GEMINI   launched by   Titan rocket

APOLLO   launched by   Saturn 5
rocket

U.S. manned spacecraft, designed on the lines of
the ballistic capsule, take the form of a cone, with
the base protected by a heat shield for reentry
through the earth's atmosphere. They evolved from
the one-seater Mercury (diameter, 6 feet; height,
7 feet; weight, 3,500 pounds) to the two-seater
Gemini (diameter, 7½ feet; height, 11 feet; weight,
4,800 pounds) and then to the three-seater moonship Apollo (diameter, 13 feet; height, 11 feet;
weight, 13,000 pounds).

be a very spectacular undertaking.

"The least one could expect was that a second ship would go up on the sixteenth orbit when the ground trace of Soyuz 1 would come back over Tyuratam [a Russian village near the Baykonur Cosmodrome, the Soviets' Cape Kennedy]. Also, the fact that a number was assigned to the ship whose name means 'Union' hinted that it would be joined by Soyuz 2."

The Soviet Union, like the United States, suddenly found itself going through a serious reevaluation of a new spaceship before it flew men again.

With the United States and the Soviet Union both in the third generation of manned spaceflight, the race to the moon hinged on rocket power.

The United States in 1966 increased the power of its Saturn 1 rocket to 1.7 million pounds of thrust and called it Saturn 1B.

The balance of rocket power shifted definitely in favor of the United States late in 1967, when Saturn 5 made its debut. Standing higher than the Statue of Liberty and weighing more than 3 000 tons, Saturn 5 lifted itself from the launch pad at Cape Kennedy with a display of rocket power greater than any heretofore produced on earth.

The giant vehicle—a composite of three separate rockets with a total thrust of 8.7 million pounds—boosted an unmanned Apollo spacecraft to a distance of 12,000 miles in space. The spacecraft, returning to earth, blazed into the atmosphere at a speed of 25,000 miles per hour—the velocity to be endured by astronauts on a return flight from the moon.

This was a decisive test for both the rocket and the spacecraft. Saturn 5 proved that it could hurl a manned vehicle toward the moon. The spacecraft proved that it could endure a fiery dash through the atmosphere on the return from the moon.

Coming from far behind at the start of the race, the United States now clearly had secured leadership. In less than a decade, American power grew from a relatively weak Vanguard rocket barely able to orbit a 21½-pound satellite to a mighty Saturn booster capable of sending nearly 50 tons toward the moon. The United States had the means to put men on the lunar surface.

For its Saturn 5, the United States had developed a single engine capable of 1.5 million pounds of thrust—as much as the entire eight-engine Saturn 1B. Five of these engines, clustered at the base of the rocket, plus powerful new hydrogen-burning engines on the two upper stages, enable Saturn 5 to launch more weight than all of the Mercury and Gemini spacecraft combined. (There were 16 of these, excluding test flights that did not carry men.)

After a long delay, on October 11, 1968, the United States finally launched the first Apollo spacecraft with a three-man crew aboard. It was the beginning of step-by-step testing of the procedure for landing on the moon.

Astronauts Walter M. Schirra, Jr., Donn F. Eisele, and R. Walter Cunningham put the Apollo 7 spacecraft through its paces for 11 days in earth orbit. They tested guidance and navigation equipment, the life-support system, and the ability to rendezvous.

The astronauts removed their bulky space suits and spent the entire 11 days working in coveralls. They even came down for a perfect landing without putting their protective pressure suits back on.

The flight of Apollo 7 restored confidence in the lunar project. Space officials now had good reason to believe that Apollo would carry Americans to the moon on schedule and ahead of the Soviets.

The major hurdle yet to be overcome was the lunar landing vehicle. A test would show whether the mother ship and the lander could rendezvous and dock and whether the engine designed to deliver two men to and from the lunar surface would work.

Within days after the first Apollo astronauts returned to earth, the Soviet Union completed its comeback from its own tragedy. An unmanned Soyuz 2 spacecraft was rocketed into earth orbit. The following day Soyuz 3, with Cosmonaut Georgi Beragovoi aboard, made a rendezvous with it.

Nearly two years after Gemini 6 and Gemini 7 met over the

Pacific, the Soviet space pilot maneuvered his craft close to the Soyuz 2 but made no attempt to dock.

Despite the cautious approach of the Soviet manned test, the race for the moon seemed suddenly to come into a new focus. It had become a race *around* the moon as well as a race to land *on* the moon. Two things happened late in 1968 to make it appear that the Soviet Union might be ready to fly men around the moon.

In September and again in November, Russia launched spacecraft called Zond 5 and 6 around the moon on a course that brought them back to landings in the Indian Ocean. The September spectacular was the first time a space vehicle had been sent to the vicinity of the moon and recovered. Top leaders in the American space program, such as von Braun, believed that Zond 5 and 6 were really Soyuz spacecraft sent on trial runs in preparation for a manned flight over the same route. The vehicles did not carry dogs, as von Braun had predicted years before, but they carried lower life forms, including small turtles.

If the Russians could be the first to send a manned flight around the moon, they could drain away a good deal of the favorable credit which the United States might expect from a first lunar landing.

A contest to determine which of the two superpowers would be first in a race around the moon was not envisaged when the master plan for the Apollo mission was laid out. At the time the lunar landing goal was established, the United States had conceded that the Russians might be the first to fly around the moon.

However, an opportunity now presented itself to surpass the Soviets in two contests—a manned race around the moon and a manned landing on the moon.

The sequence was this: Initially, after the success of Apollo 7, NASA had planned to test in a single experiment the two key elements to be used in a moon landing—the command ship and the lunar taxi. The test was to be in the nature of a "dry run" for a moon flight except that it would be conducted in earth

Page from a Lunar Flight Plan

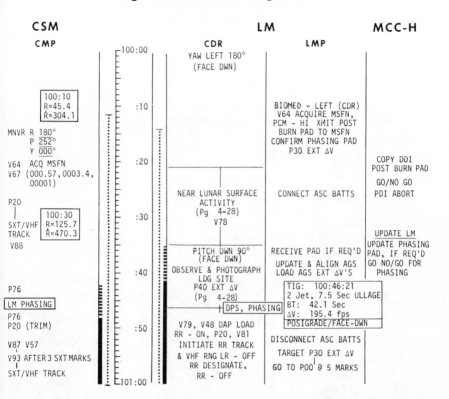

CSM	LM		MCC-H
CMP	CDR	LMP	

CSM — **CMP**

100:10
R=45.4
Ṙ=304.1

MNVR R 180°
     P 252̄°
     Y 000̄°

V64 ACQ MSFN
V67 (000.57,0003.4,
00001)

P20

100:30
SXT/VHF | R=125.7
TRACK | Ṙ=470.3

V88

P76

LM PHASING

P76
P20 (TRIM)

V87 V57

V93 AFTER 3 SXT MARKS

SXT/VHF TRACK

Timeline scale: 100:00, :10, :20, :30, :40, :50, 101:00

LM — **CDR**

YAW LEFT 180°
(FACE DWN)

NEAR LUNAR SURFACE
ACTIVITY
(Pg 4-28)
V78

PITCH DWN 90°
(FACE DWN)
OBSERVE & PHOTOGRAPH
LDG SITE
P40 EXT ΔV
(Pg 4-28)

V79, V48 DAP LOAD
RR - ON, P20, V81
INITIATE RR TRACK
& VHF RNG LR - OFF
RR DESIGNATE,
RR - OFF

LMP

BIOMED - LEFT (CDR)
V64 ACQUIRE MSFN,
PCM - HI XMIT POST
BURN PAD TO MSFN
CONFIRM PHASING PAD
P30 EXT ΔV

CONNECT ASC BATTS

RECEIVE PAD IF REQ'D

UPDATE & ALIGN AGS
LOAD AGS EXT ΔV'S

DPS, PHASING

| TIG: 100:46:21 |
| 2 Jet, 7.5 Sec ULLAGE |
| BT: 42.1 Sec |
| ΔV: 195.4 fps |
| POSIGRADE/FACE-DWN |

DISCONNECT ASC BATTS

TARGET P30 EXT ΔV

GO TO P00 @ 5 MARKS

MCC-H

COPY DOI
POST BURN PAD

GO/NO GO
PDI ABORT

UPDATE LM
UPDATE PHASING
PAD, IF REQ'D
GO NO/GO FOR
PHASING

On their flight to and from the moon, astronauts carry a book-length
Flight Plan which tells each what he must do, minute by minute. Instructions are written in "space language." For example, the page reproduced
above, programming 60 minutes from hour 100:00 (5 days after leaving
earth) to hour 101:00, has the Command Module Pilot (CMP) circling the
moon in the Command Service Module (CSM) while his colleagues, the
Commander (CDR) and the Lunar Module Pilot (LMP), are maneuvering
their Lunar Module (LM) for a landing on the moon. At 100:15, CMP, reading the left column, maneuvers by rolling 180° and pitching 252° with no
change in yaw (MNVR R 180° P 252° Y 000°). At 100:35, CDR (next column) pitches down 90°, face down, preparing to photograph the landing
site. At 100:10, LMP checks CDR's medical harness (BIOMED—LEFT
CDR) and contacts Houston (V 64 ACQUIRE MSFN). Mission Control
Center—Houston (MCC-H) records data concerning a previous rocket
burn (COPY DOI POST BURN) and later reaches the moment to decide
whether to go ahead for next burn (GO NO/GO FOR PHASING).

The First Men in Space

U.S. Apollo Program

Apollo 7 / *Oct. 11, 1968*
163 Orbits

Walter M. Schirra, Jr.

Donn F. Eisele

R. Walter Cunningham

Apollo 8 / *Dec. 21, 1968*
10 Orbits of the Moon

Frank Borman

James A. Lovell, Jr.

William A. Anders

Apollo 9 / *March 3, 1969*
151 Orbits

James A. McDivitt

David R. Scott

Russell L. Schweickart

Apollo 10 / *May 18, 1969* | Apollo 11 / *July 1969* | Apollo 12 / *Sept. 1969*

Tom P. Stafford

Neil A. Armstrong

Charles Conrad, Jr.

John W. Young

Michael Collins

Richard F. Gordon, Jr.

Eugene A. Cernan

Edwin E. Aldrin, Jr.

Alan L. Bean

orbit rather than lunar orbit so that the astronauts could get back more quickly if something went wrong.

However, engineers at Cape Kennedy fell behind in getting the lunar landing craft ready for the test. Rather than hold up a second Apollo launch, NASA decided to use the available Saturn 5 rocket for something else—a manned flight of the command ship (without the landing craft) around the moon.

This was the origin of Apollo 8. As preparations were being made to send the first Americans around the moon and back to earth, there was an air of expectation that Moscow might announce at any moment that Soviet cosmonauts already were on their way. However, the Soviet moon flight did not materialize.

Apollo 8 blasted off on December 21, 1968, on a mission that captured the imagination of the world as had no single space effort before. With communications satellites carrying television pictures of the flight all over the world, NASA estimated that one-half to two-thirds of all humanity heard or read about the epic flight by Astronauts Frank Borman, James A. Lovell, Jr., and William A. Anders.

News coverage was telecast in the Soviet Union, and even Havana radio carried reports from the Voice of America. Cape Kennedy was filled with more newspaper correspondents than it had seen since the flight in 1962 of John Glenn. Congratulations poured in from around the world as the astronauts flew toward the moon.

On Christmas Eve, they were circling just 69 miles above the moon's surface, looking directly at sites chosen for the first manned landings. From its launch until it returned to earth nearly a week later, Apollo 8's performance was perfection itself.

The flight showed beyond any doubt that the Apollo command spacecraft was ready for its part of the lunar landing flight. The only remaining piece to be fitted into the puzzle was the landing vehicle. While Borman, Lovell, and Anders were relating details of their flight to NASA officials, an Apollo spacecraft carrying the landing craft for a test flight in earth orbit was moved to its Cape Kennedy launch pad. The subsequent successful flight of Apollo 9 proved that the lunar taxi, too, was ready for its critical role.

Less than a month after the flight of Apollo 8, the Soviet Union put two more Soyuz vehicles in orbit. Soyuz 4 carried a single pilot, and Soyuz 5 carried three cosmonauts.

They made a rendezvous in orbit, and for the first time in space history, two manned vehicles docked. Cosmonauts Yevgeny Khrunov and Aleksei Yeliseyev accomplished another space first for the Soviet Union by walking in space from Soyuz 5 to join the lone pilot in Soyuz 4.

The Russians called the connected vehicles "the world's first experimental space station," and they said that this would lead to permanent orbiting outposts which would be supplied by shuttle vehicles operating between the stations and earth.

However, the Soviet achievement, described by American experts as only "a slight step forward" in manned flight, could not upset the fact that Apollo's manned flight around the moon had put the United States well out in front. The Russians might still try for "a snatch of some lunar stuff" by an unmanned mission, but their chances of having Soviet citizens plant the red flag on the moon before the Americans could get there with the Stars and Stripes were now believed virtually to have vanished.

Some observers at this time suggested that the Soviet Union

The First Men in Space

U.S.S.R. Soyuz Program

Soyuz 1 / *April 23, 1967*
17 Orbits

Vladimir M. Komarov

Soyuz 3 / *Oct. 26, 1968*
64 Orbits

Georgi T. Beragovoi

might be rearranging the objectives of its space program, playing down Soviet interest in putting men on the moon to soften the propaganda setback of not getting there first. Nevertheless, some top NASA officials remained convinced that the Russians were as determined as the Americans to land men on the moon as soon as possible.

By docking manned space vehicles in earth orbit, Russia proved that it was mastering the techniques for putting together a large space station or sending a manned ship from earth orbit to the moon. The space station approach might offer the Soviets an opportunity to take the lead in another important area of space technology.

Though the United States was now well ahead in the race to the moon, the Soviet Union remained a formidable contender for supremacy elsewhere in space, both for military and civilian purposes.

The intensity of Soviet activity is indicated by the amount of payload the Russians are putting into space. According to an estimate by Dr. Sheldon, the Soviet Union placed 3.3 million pounds of payload in space by the end of 1968. This compares with 2.7 million pounds for the United States.

Furthermore, during the first part of 1969 the Soviet Union launched a greater number of space vehicles than did the United States.

Clearly, the race in space is far from over.

CHAPTER TWELVE

The Outlook in Space

After securing a foothold on the moon, Americans face this question: What next?

They are divided in their answers, just as they were divided over the issue of going to the moon in the first place. Some would like to have us develop our moon beachhead into a major colony—a permanent lunar base from which to plunge still deeper into space, to neighboring Mars and Venus, and then to more distant planets. Others reply that this would be a luxury we cannot afford, that the costs of curing our social and physical ills on earth are much too high for us to indulge in ambitious expeditions in space.

Increasing demands on taxpayers' pocketbooks, combined with the "hidden tax" of inflation, have had the effect of cooling earlier enthusiasm for NASA.

The vast sums given to the space agency during the 12 years following Sputnik 1 were justified by a need to meet the Soviet challenge in this new dimension of the Cold War. Congress has advanced about $24 billion to cover the cost of the entire manned spaceflight program to date. The cost of a single trip to the moon and back in an Apollo spaceship is at least $350 million.

The price tag for sending astronauts on to orbit Mars and Venus would undoubtedly be even greater. Round trips to these planets would last eight or nine months or more depending on the distance from the earth at launch time. Men could not endure the physical and psychological hardships over such a period in quarters as cramped as those used in the Apollo moon missions. Also, a spacecraft of the Apollo type and size could not carry enough food and oxygen to last for so many months.

This means that a larger spacecraft would be required—one launched by a rocket far more powerful than the giant Saturn 5 used for moon missions. The prospect before Congress and the taxpayer becomes one of skyrocketing budgets for a constantly expanding space program.

The almost automatic reaction is to call for a cutback after the landing on the moon. If the U.S. goal was to prove that we could beat the Russians to that achievement, many ask why we should continue to give NASA such large sums.

Appropriations must be made some time in advance, and the issue over future expenditures in space heated up even before U.S. astronauts took the Apollo into space for its first orbital test. James E. Webb, who was put in charge of NASA when President Kennedy announced the moon landing goal in 1961, resigned in autumn 1968 in protest against cuts in the space program.

NASA's annual budget, after reaching a peak of $5.9 billion in 1966, was cut to $3.87 billion for 1969.

While there is considerable disagreement over the amount we should be spending, there is little doubt that we are committed to space for an indefinite period. We were committed by the fact that technological and political developments have turned space into a new arena of military, strategic, and scientific competition.

A first-class power today cannot remain a first-class power without a considerable commitment in space—if only from the standpoint of national security. There is no reason to believe that either the United States or the Soviet Union proposes to renounce its position as a first-class power. And there is no

The Solar System

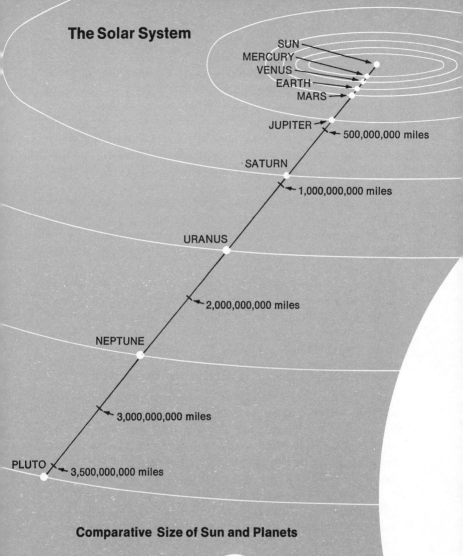

SUN
MERCURY
VENUS
EARTH
MARS
JUPITER
← 500,000,000 miles
SATURN
← 1,000,000,000 miles
URANUS
← 2,000,000,000 miles
NEPTUNE
← 3,000,000,000 miles
PLUTO ← 3,500,000,000 miles

Comparative Size of Sun and Planets

PLUTO NEPTUNE URANUS SATURN JUPITER MARS EARTH VENUS MERCURY SUN

reason to believe that either will withdraw from its basic commitment to a strong position in space.

The question, then, is: How far and how fast will the two
superpowers push ahead in this new arena? The answer will depend to a great extent on the economic sacrifices that each country is ready to make in order to pay the tremendous costs involved. And the extent of those sacrifices will depend, in turn,
on the intensity of the continuing race in space.

We already have seen how rapidly the space race has es-
calated. The early Soviet successes in orbiting satellites and then
in putting men in space led to a reaction by the United States
to overtake and to surpass the Russians. It was this reaction
which carried us to the moon.

The Soviet Union cannot be expected to remain quiet and to
settle for second place in space. Each important achievement
by the United States almost certainly will generate pressure in
Moscow to match or to surpass it. National defense and national
pride ride along with each rocket sent into space, and these
are powerful forces for escalation.

The Soviet Union at any moment could produce a new sur-
prise to recover its lead in space. Soviet development of a giant
rocket for an intercontinental ballistic missile—said to be capable
of delivering a multimegaton thermonuclear warhead—touched
off calls in the United States for a new defense against the threat
of a "first strike" by Russia, using this formidable new weapon,
the SS-9. The result was a proposal that we spend $6 billion
or $7 billion on an anti-ballistic-missile system to protect the
Minuteman missiles on which we rely to deter the Russians.

At the same time, it was widely rumored that the Russians
would use their newly expanded rocket power for further advances in space. This again illustrated the close interrelationship
between military and civilian space activities. And it suggested
that a response by the United States to meet a new move by the
Soviet Union in one area might well be followed by a response
to meet a new move in another.

Russia's growing rocket power is frequently cited to support
speculation in the Western world that Moscow plans to under-

take manned flights to the planets. This would be a form of "one-upmanship" in space. For example, if the United States by landing on the moon appears to be "one up" on the Soviet Union, the latter tries to go us one better with a mission to Mars or Venus, or both.

But this "game," as was said earlier, is closely related to military, strategic, and scientific developments. Whoever is ahead evidently feels he has demonstrated his superiority in war and science. On the basis of such superiority, it is feared that the Soviet Union might make unacceptable demands on the United States and the free world. That is why many Americans insist on denying Russia superiority.

Should the Soviet Union extend the space race to Mars and Venus by flying men to these planets, it is likely that the United States would move in the same direction. The United States could not ignore a Soviet planetary flight in the 1970s any more than it could ignore the presence of Sputnik in the 1950s. That could mean that the annual NASA budget, which critics would like to hold to $3 billion or less, could climb back to $5 billion or more.

It is reasonable to conclude, then, that our expenditures in space will depend not on what Congress desires to grant, but rather on how much the Soviet Union decides to spend. If the Soviet people are willing to let their leaders invest more and more rubles in space at the cost of a continued low standard of living, then the American people may see their own expenditures go up by an even greater percentage to maintain the U.S. lead.

It is difficult to make a meaningful comparison between the space budgets of the United States and the Soviet Union. In the first place, it is almost impossible to determine how much the Russians really are spending. The United States draws a distinction between military and civilian space activities. In the Soviet Union, these are so closely interrelated that funds for an ostensibly civilian program, such as a flight to Mars, might easily come from the military budget. This leaves aside the point of whether published Soviet figures can be taken at face value.

Once we take a given figure of Soviet expenditures, we come up against the problem of translating rubles into dollars. The official rate established by the Soviet Union (1 ruble equals $1.11) is an arbitrary one which is not necessarily related to the purchasing power of Soviet currency.

We can establish what the ruble is worth in the amount of meat, bread, vegetables, shoes, clothing, and other consumer goods it will buy. But how are we to determine how much the ruble is worth in the amount of metal, fuel, computers, and other equipment which go into a Soviet rocket and spacecraft? Under its tight, centrally controlled economy, the Soviet government can assign any price it chooses to any article, so that the cost items in the Soviet space budget may be considered to represent little more than arbitrary bookkeeping entries.

Comparisons of U.S. and Soviet spending on space, therefore, are little more than educated guesses. One such guess, made by Dr. Sheldon, is that the Soviet Union is spending about 2 percent of its gross national product (the total value of a nation's goods and services), as compared with about two-thirds of 1 percent by the United States.

A more moderate spending program for a more leisurely advance into space probably could come only through a basic understanding between the United States and the Soviet Union. However, in view of the fact that advances in space technology are now closely related to a nation's military-strategic capability, we can hardly expect an understanding on space unless we first have an understanding on what is happening on the ground. In other words, an agreement must first be reached to end the cold war on earth.

Although negotiations on disarmament may continue year after year, as they have in the past, we can hardly expect a fundamental change in Soviet policy in the near future, and the United States faces the prospect of a continuation of cold war —on earth and in space—in one degree or another.

This made it necessary for the U.S. government to devise a space program which met two conditions:

The program had to be a long-term one which would sustain the momentum already achieved by Project Apollo and preserve our leadership position. A short-term approach, according to NASA officials, would be ineffective and costly. Space systems, becoming more complex, require more time to design, develop, and test. NASA planners say it would have taken many more years to reach the moon if we had undertaken Project Apollo on a year-to-year basis.

The space policy had to pay close attention to the high costs involved in development of this new technology and to the great reluctance of many Americans to divert large sums for it from urgent social, educational, and health problems.

Shortly after the November 1968 elections, President Nixon asked prominent scientists to make a preliminary assessment of the future of the U.S. space program. This was considered advisable in view of the uncertainty about space policy caused by congressional budget cuts.

A task force of space experts was set up under the leadership of Dr. Charles H. Townes of the University of California at Berkeley, formerly of the Massachusetts Institute of Technology, and Dr. Lee A. DuBridge, then President of the California Institute of Technology, now the President's science adviser. The task force's report to the President recommended a strong space program, along with techniques for reducing the costs of getting to and from a future space station or base on the moon.

This formula, in effect, sought to meet the conditions mentioned earlier: (1) a long-term program; (2) proper regard to economies, wherever possible.

After receiving the report, President Nixon appointed a panel of scientists and government officials to develop a new space program for the next decade. The panel included NASA Administrator Thomas O. Paine; Secretary of the Air Force Robert C. Seamans, Jr.; Vice-President Spiro T. Agnew, chairman of the National Aeronautics and Space Council; and DuBridge.

The new program may provide for continued exploration of the moon by different teams of American astronauts and scientists; further steps toward setting up a space station (which would match the space station reportedly being planned by the Soviet Union); development of a shuttle to fly between the earth and the space station, servicing the latter with the supplies needed from earth; and development of a "big, dumb booster" as a more economical means of lifting cargo into space.

Another economy would be postponement of manned missions to the other planets, for the time being at least, in favor of unmanned missions. Unmanned spacecraft with television cameras and instruments to sample the environments of Venus and Mars already have skirted those planets and have transmitted a good deal of new information about them. For example, Mariner spacecraft revealed that temperatures on Venus run as high as 800 degrees F.—too high to permit life as we know it.

Achievements of this kind helped to support the case for continuation of unmanned missions and for putting off vastly more expensive manned missions. A number of scientists, including Dr. James Van Allen, say that unmanned missions in space can prove about as effective as manned missions.

To meet some of the criticism against a costly space program, NASA may intensify the number and activity of satellites with goals on earth. These satellites would again demonstrate how the American taxpayer is getting an immediate return on his investment in the form of better weather forecasting, better communications, and surveys of natural resources.

However, the heart of the NASA program centers around manned exploration of space and efforts closely related to it. To sustain this program, NASA officials say they need at least $3 billion annually. This would mean a total of $30 billion for space development during the decade of the 1970s.

While the amount of money appropriated for space may vary from year to year and the arguments between NASA's supporters and opponents are certain to continue, the pattern of development is becoming clear.

In years ahead, we are almost certain to see more and more astronauts and cosmonauts shooting through space. They will

An unmanned Mariner spacecraft, ready to take off on a scouting mission to Mars. Its reconnaissance work is the planetary counterpart of lunar surveys by other robots.

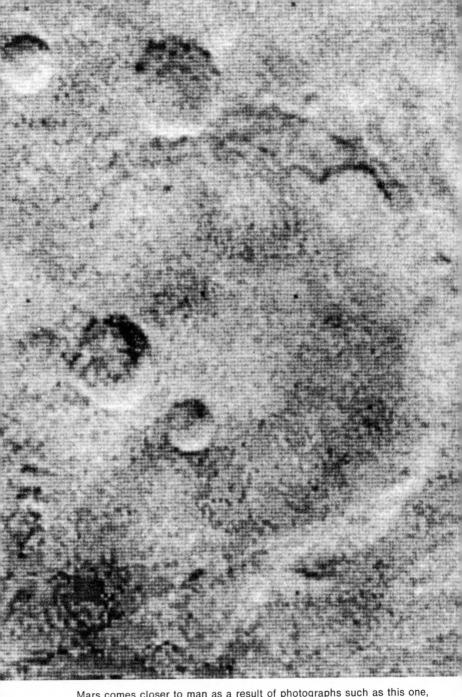

Mars comes closer to man as a result of photographs such as this one, taken by Mariner 4, covering an area of 170 miles by 150 miles.

be operating from bases in their own countries and from bases on the moon and orbiting space stations.

American scientists believe it will be possible to fly men to Mars in a decade or so. They now are studying systems for producing food aboard large space vehicles.

They also are working on a project which would increase the power of the Saturn 5 rocket and thereby the weight of the payload it could launch. And they expect to develop systems of power that would enable spaceships to travel hundreds of thousands of miles per hour.

However powerful the rockets, chemical propulsion will never be able to take manned flights much beyond Mars or Venus. The bigger the chemical rocket, the greater its fuel tank must be, because this type of rocket consumes fuel at such a rapid rate that it can fire only for a short time. Its brief, tremendous bursts of energy provide just about enough acceleration, at best, to enable a spacecraft to reach Mars or Venus.

To carry man still deeper into space, scientists are working on compact, long-operating systems which would push spaceships to fantastic speeds once they have escaped earth's gravity. One possibility is to harness the thrust produced by light. Another promising source is a small, nuclear-powered unit.

These developments and their implications for extensive exploration of the solar system are somewhere in the future. The major, immediate problem is to reduce the cost of boosting payloads into earth orbit.

In the early days of the U.S. space program, the cost of orbiting some of our satellites was $1 million per pound. As rockets grew more powerful, the cost per pound dropped. Saturn 5 can push 280,000 pounds into an orbit near the earth, reducing payload cost to about $500 per pound. This is a great improvement over the early Vanguard rockets, but it does not go far enough. Space economists estimate that the cost must drop to one tenth this amount, or even a hundredth, before it will be economical to use nearby space for manufacturing or for permanently manned scientific facilities that could be resupplied from earth.

It is difficult to see how freight rates in space can be reduced much more, but Wernher von Braun, who has worked with rockets from the V-2 to the Saturn 5, says:

"It is believed that someday we are going to have reusable vehicles that can be scheduled like freighters. And the cost per pound of freight delivered into orbit will come down to compare with the price today for cargo between Japan and Europe or the United States.

"We definitely are not locked in a situation for all eternity in which costs are prohibitive. They are costly today, but as better transportation systems become available, it is definitely possible to reduce these costs."

There are two ways of doing this. One is to develop the big, dumb booster as an inexpensive rocket for carrying only cargo. The other is to build a machine that can be recovered after each use.

A rocket such as the Saturn 5 is extremely expensive—for two reasons. First, it must carry men, and this requires the highest degree of reliability that twentieth-century engineering can produce. Almost all of its vital parts are backed up by identical parts to take over in case of failure. It is designed to be as nearly fail-safe as so complex a machine can be. Before it is flown, its stages are clamped to earth and test-fired. They must work as precisely as they are expected to in space.

The second reason is that every rocket developed so far is used only once. The first two stages of a Saturn 5 fall into the sea after firing, and the third is left in orbit as a piece of "space junk."

Many studies have been made of the possibility of recovering rockets from the ocean. Engineers believe that several dozen Saturns would have to be launched annually before it would be economical to develop means to lower them gently into the sea, where they could be recovered and used again.

A big, dumb booster would not have all the fail-safe equipment of a Saturn 5. Instead of a highly refined machine, it would be exactly what its name suggests: a powerful but crude booster put together in the fashion of a steam boiler. It might

A design for a Manned Orbiting Laboratory, expected to go into service during the decade of the 1970s.

not even have to be test-fired before being launched.

The booster would cost only a fraction as much as present-day rockets of similar size and would haul freight much more economically than rockets built before. It probably would be an intermediate step before achievement of the space shuttle, which would put an end to the loss of rockets after a single launching.

For some years now, engineers have dreamed of a space vehicle that could take off and land like a conventional airplane, but they could not solve the problem of getting the vehicle safely back through the earth's atmosphere. In the early 1960s, the Air Force worked on a vehicle called "Dyna-Soar," which was to have been boosted into orbit by a rocket and would have landed as an airplane does. It had wings which would have permitted it to skip in and out of the atmosphere and eventually come down safely on a landing site.

The project was dropped by the Defense Department in favor of a Manned Orbiting Laboratory—a satellite the size of a van to be equipped as a spacecraft for the Air Force. Details of the Manned Orbiting Laboratory are highly secret. The Air Force explains that the project is designed to determine man's ability to work in space. However, NASA already has shown how man can function in space, at least on short flights.

The Air Force evidently plans to use the laboratory as a reconnaissance satellite. It would be launched into a polar orbit, rather than around the earth's equator, where Mercury, Gemini, and Apollo spacecraft and most scientific satellites orbit. A polar orbit permits occupants to see nearly all of the earth's surface during each 24 hours.

The concept of the Air Force's defunct Dyna-Soar has now been revived, on a grander scale, for civilian use. Engineers foresee in the 1970s a rocket-launched vehicle which will take as many as nine passengers into orbit with several tons of cargo. On return to earth, it would land as an airplane does. Such a spacecraft, being reusable, might be able to reduce launch costs to $50 per pound. It could be in operation in 1976, according to Dr. George C. Mueller, head of NASA's Manned Spaceflight Program.

With projects limited to such hardware as the space shuttle and the big, dumb booster for the near future, it may be many years before the United States will need a rocket larger than Saturn 5. Smaller rockets are likely to be used in building a huge, semipermanent space station where a dozen or more people would work. It will be easier and cheaper to launch different parts of a space station and put them together in orbit than to build a new vehicle to carry all sections up in one or two launches. If one small rocket failed to reach orbit with the materials, there would be less loss of equipment than if a single monster rocket failed.

A basic space station built in the 1970s probably would be quite small. Perhaps only two sections would be flown into space and assembled. One might provide living quarters for several scientist-astronauts; the other might contain laboratory

Telstar, the satellite serving man in the field of communications.

Tiros (Television Infrared Observation Satellite), in this artist's sketch, spots and photographs a hurricane, giving man on earth advance warning of what to expect from the weather.

and research equipment. Other sections could be added later.

Large space stations of the future, as foreseen by scientists of the United States, Russia, and other nations, could be designed like enormous wheels, spinning as they orbit the earth. The rotation would create an artificial gravity through centrifugal force. (If you hold a bucket of water by the handle and swing your arm in a circle, centrifugal force keeps the water in the bucket.)

The spin of a wheel-shaped space station would create in the rim the equivalent of earth gravity so that crewmen would feel their normal weight and move about naturally. However, because of the nature of centrifugal force, objects in the hub of the wheel would remain weightless. Living quarters would be placed in the rim, and experiments might be conducted in the center. It is estimated that building such a station might cost about $10 billion.

Another project calls for orbiting large telescopes. Astronomer-astronauts in these orbiting observatories would be able to study the universe without interference from the earth's turbulent, dusty, moisture-laden atmosphere. Their laboratory could become a semipermanent facility. The small, unmanned astronomical satellites used at present function for periods of a few months. They are limited by their size in the kinds of observations they can make.

In a related field, the Space Science Board of the National Academy of Sciences has recommended launching into orbit a radio telescope with an antenna measuring as much as 12 miles in diameter. It would be assembled in space like a gigantic erector set.

As one step toward a permanent space station, NASA is projecting an orbital workshop. It would be installed in the empty fuel tank of a spent rocket.

At the time of the first landing on the moon, the United States inventory included 17 Saturn rockets for its Apollo Applications program and for continued exploration of the moon. According to this plan, one Saturn would boost its second stage into orbit. Another would launch a manned Apollo spacecraft to rendezvous and dock with the empty rocket casing. Astronauts would crawl through a tunnel from Apollo into the tank.

The rocket tank, which engineers have nicknamed the "manned can," is nearly 22 feet in diameter and 59 feet long. Three astronauts would have nearly 10,000 cubic feet of space in which to live and conduct experiments aimed at giving insights into problems of developing a full-fledged space station.

The astronauts would be able to remove their cumbersome space suits and work in coveralls in a normal atmosphere, just as they do in the Apollo spacecraft. Because of the spaciousness of the workshop, they would be able, for the first time, to evaluate fully the long-term problems of working in weightlessness. They would test experimental equipment designed to make life more comfortable for workers of the future who might stay in space stations for months at a time.

A solar telescope could be mounted in the workshop, and astronomers could study that portion of the sun's radiation which never reaches earth because the atmosphere filters it out.

The first group might stay in the workshop for a little less than a month, then reboard Apollo and return to earth. A second team might live in the workshop for nearly two months. NASA officials believe it might be possible for teams of men to orbit in such a workshop for as long as a year.

All of these projects, added to those on Soviet drawing boards, provide an idea of what may lie ahead—a panorama of man moving out into the firmament, discovering and encircling not just one new world, as Columbus and Magellan did, but many new worlds. It staggers the imagination, but the human mind is beginning to adjust, as it usually does to changing reality.

This new adventure in space raises one big question: Where will it lead man in his relations with other men?

Man was first attracted toward the sky by innocent curiosity. Then he propelled himself into space while searching for better ways of waging war. In the process, he opened a door through which we can pass to discover and inspect, first-hand, a world of many worlds.

Perhaps this physical approach to other worlds can produce

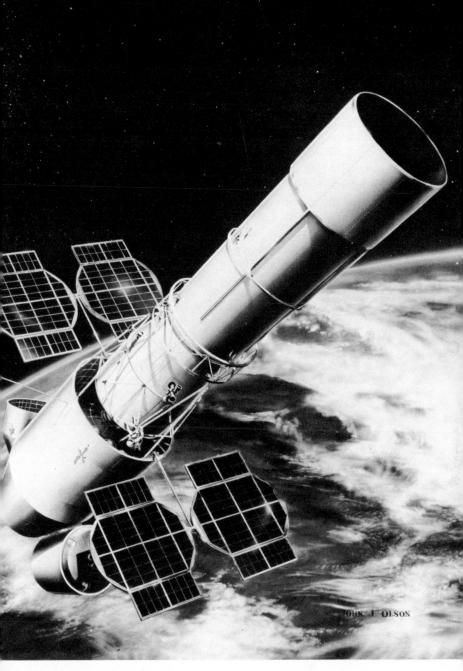

An artist's concept of a Manned Orbiting Astronomical Telescope, which will extend man's sight to new worlds.

a new perspective on man's position in relation to his earth and on earth's position in relation to other heavenly bodies. The picture of earth taken by our astronauts as they circled the moon already has enabled us to see ourselves as beings from elsewhere in the universe might see us.

Never before have we been able to see our planet thus—a colorful agate spinning in the inky vacuum of space—one of an infinite number of celestial bodies. Will such a perspective shrink man's vanity and induce a humility which might bring peace at last to an earth now menaced by nuclear destruction? Will we someday witness the irony of man's finding in space the peace he could not find on earth?

Time and space will tell.

A Brief History of Flight

c. 2000 B.C. Wan Pou, a scholar in Chinese legend, constructs a kite device, propelled by 47 rockets; explodes during takeoff.

1232 A.D. First record of a rocket device, used for military purposes by the Chinese.

1485 Leonardo da Vinci researches possibilities of flight, builds aircraft models.

1543 Nicholas Copernicus publishes *On the Revolutions of the Celestial Orbs*, stating that the sun is the center of our universe.

1609 Johannes Kepler publishes *On the Motions of Mars*, defining the laws of planetary motion.

1610 Galileo Galilei publishes *Messenger of the Stars*, reporting that the moon and planets are "other worlds." His observations establish the science of astronomy.

1649 Cyrano de Bergerac, in *The Comic History of the States and Empires of the Moon and the Sun*, is the first to propose rockets as a means of propulsion for going to the moon.

1687   Sir Isaac Newton publishes his *Principia*, stating the laws of motion and gravity.

1783   First manned flight in a balloon by Pilatre de Rogier, Marquis d'Arlandres.

1790   The Ruggieri family of Italy launches small animals attached to rockets and lands them safely by parachute to advertise its fireworks.

1801   Sir William Congreve conducts first systematic study of rockets. He is responsible for the "rockets' red glare" at Fort McHenry during the War of 1812.

1810   George Cayley, of England, builds and flies the first successful manned glider.

1903   Orville and Wilbur Wright are the first to fly a powered airplane.

        K. E. Tsiolkovsky, of Russia, publishes the first calculations concerning the possibilities of putting artificial satellites into earth orbit.

1919   Robert Goddard, of the United States, publishes *A Method of Reaching Extreme Altitudes*, opening a new era in modern rocket research.

1926   Goddard develops and launches the first liquid-propellant rocket.

1929   Hermann Oberth, an Austrian, publishes *The Way to Space Travel*, stating the fundamental problems of spaceflight.

        Fritz von Opel, of Germany, flies the first manned rocket-propelled glider.

1930   The German Rocket Society begins experiments, which later lead to development of the V-2.

1933   Dr. Eugene Sanger, an Austrian, begins research in Germany aimed at developing the rocket motor for airplane flight.

1939   The first jet-propelled airplane is flown in Germany.

1944   Germany fires its V-2 ballistic missile against England. It weighs 12½ tons and can reach altitudes of almost 100 miles. Wernher von Braun is the chief engineer.

1957   Soviet Union fires the first intercontinental ballistic missile (ICBM) on August 26.

Sputnik 1 is launched by the Soviet Union on October 4, ushering in the space age. It is the first man-made satellite to orbit the earth; weighs 184 pounds.

The Soviet Union orbits Sputnik 2 on November 3. This second artificial satellite weighs 1,120 pounds and carries the first living creature into space, a dog named Laika.

1958   Explorer 1, the first U.S. earth satellite, is launched on January 31; weighs 30.8 pounds and discovers the Van Allen radiation belts which surround earth.

Vanguard 1, the second U.S. satellite, goes into orbit on March 17. It weighs 3.25 pounds and continues to transmit information for more than six years; should remain in orbit for about a century.

Explorer 3, the third U.S. satellite, lifts off on March 26. It is designed as a space probe to expand the information gathered by Explorer 1.

The Soviet Union orbits Sputnik 3 on May 15. It weighs 2,925 pounds.

On October 1, NASA assumes responsibility for the peaceful space research and development of the United States.

1959   Russia's Luna 1 undertakes the first lunar probe on January 2. It passes within 4,000 miles of the moon and goes into orbit around the sun, becoming the first man-made planet.

Vanguard 2, February 17, sends back the first photographs of earth's cloud cover.

1959   Vanguard 3, weighing about 100 pounds, takes off
            on September 18 and transmits information to earth
            for 84 days.

            On September 13, Luna 2, weighing 86 pounds, be-
            comes the first man-made object to reach the sur-
            face of the moon.

            The Soviet Union launches Luna 3 on October 4.
            It sends back the first photographs of the hidden
            side of the moon.

1960   Sputnik 4, weighing 10,008 pounds, is placed in
            earth orbit on May 15.

            Sputnik 5 carries two dogs, Belka and Strelka, into
            orbit on August 19, and returns them safely to earth.

1961   On April 12, Cosmonaut Yuri A. Gagarin becomes
            the first man in space. His craft Vostok 1, weigh-
            ing 10,417 pounds, completes 1 orbit and returns
            to earth after 1 hour, 48 minutes.

            Alan B. Shepard, Jr., becomes the first American in
            space on May 5. His suborbital flight in the Mer-
            cury-Redstone 3 lasts 15 minutes.

            Virgil I. Grissom tests the Mercury-Redstone 4 in
            another suborbital mission on July 21. The flight
            lasts 16 minutes.

            Gherman S. Titov, flying the Vostok 2, completes
            17 earth orbits on August 6-7. The flight covers 25
            hours, 18 minutes.

            The United States tests its first Ranger satellite on
            August 23. The series is designed to perfect the two-
            stage launch and long-range communications
            (telemetry), and to gather information from the
            moon by depositing a capsule named "Tonto" on
            the lunar surface.

1962   John H. Glenn, Jr., is the first American in earth orbit, February 20; completes 3 orbits in his capsule, Friendship 7. His Mercury-Atlas 6 flight lasts 4 hours, 55 minutes.

Ranger 4 becomes the first U.S. spacecraft to land on the moon, April 26.

The Mercury-Atlas 7 carrying M. Scott Carpenter completes 3 earth orbits on May 24. His capsule Aurora 7 lands 250 miles from target.

The Soviet Union stages the first group flight as Vostok 3 and Vostok 4, each weighing 10,500 pounds, pass within 3.1 miles of each other on August 12. Vostok 3's mission lasts 94 hours, 22 minutes, manned by Andrian G. Nikolayev. Vostok 4's mission with Pavel R. Popovitch takes 70 hours, 57 minutes.

Walter M. Shirra, Jr., flying Mercury-Atlas 8 completes 6 orbits on October 3. After 9 hours, 13 minutes in flight he lands 5 miles from his target.

1963   L. Gordon Cooper, Jr., completes 22 earth orbits in Mercury-Atlas 9 on May 15-16. The flight lasts 34 hours, 20 minutes.

Vostok 5, launched on June 14 with Valery F. Bykovsky, and Vostok 6, launched on June 16, pass within 3 miles of each other during orbit. Vostok 6 carries Valentina V. Tereshkova, the first woman to enter space.

1964   The Soviet Union's Voskhod 1 carries Vladimir M. Komarov, Konstantin P. Feokistov, and Dr. Boris G. Yegorov into orbit on October 12. The flight lasts 24 hours, 17 minutes, completing 16 earth orbits.

1965   On March 18, Aleksei A. Leonov becomes the first man to take a "space walk" outside his craft, the Voskhod 2. The walk lasts 10 minutes; the craft is manned by Pavel I. Belyayev.

1965   Virgil I. Grissom and John W. Young in Gemini 3
        undertake the first manned orbital maneuvers on
        March 23. The flight completes its mission of 3
        earth orbits in 4 hours, 53 minutes.

        Edward H. White II is the first American to walk
        in space, during Gemini 4's flight with James A.
        McDivitt, June 3-7. He remains outside the craft
        for 21 minutes; the total mission is completed in 97
        hours, 48 minutes.

        Gemini 5, carrying astronauts L. Gordon Cooper,
        Jr., and Charles Conrad, Jr., August 21-29, com-
        pletes 120 orbits in 190 hours, 56 minutes.

        December 4-18, Frank Borman and James A. Lo-
        vell, Jr., in Gemini 7, complete 206 orbits. The
        Gemini 6-A, launched December 15 with Walter
        M. Shirra, Jr., and Tom P. Stafford, passes within
        1 foot of Gemini 7.

1966   On June 2, the United States fires the first of its
        Surveyor series, launched by an Atlas-Centaur
        rocket. Surveyor 1, weighing 2,200 pounds and
        carrying 60 pounds of equipment, is designed to
        make a "soft" lunar landing. It sends back 11,000
        photographs.

        The flight mission of Gemini 9-A, June 3-6, manned
        by Tom P. Stafford and Eugene A. Cernan, includes
        rendezvous, extravehicular activity, and a precision
        landing.

        Gemini 10, July 18-21, with John W. Young and
        Michael Collins, rendezvous with two targets.

        The techniques of rendezvous and docking are tested
        by Charles Conrad, Jr., and Richard F. Gordon, Jr.,
        in Gemini 11, September 12-15.

        Flying Gemini 12, November 11-15, James A. Lo-
        vell, Jr., and Edwin E. Aldrin, Jr., complete 59
        earth orbits in 94 hours, 33 minutes.

1968   Apollo 7, carrying Walter M. Schirra, Jr., Donn F. Eisele, and R. Walter Cunningham, completes 163 earth orbits, October 11-22; the lift-off weight is 45,374 pounds. It is the first manned flight for the spacecraft which will carry man to the moon.

Soyuz 3, carrying Georgi T. Beragovoi, is fired October 26; makes a rendezvous with unmanned Soyuz 2. The flight lasts 95 hours.

Frank Borman, James A. Lovell, Jr., and William A. Anders, in Apollo 8, are the first men to orbit the moon. They complete 10 orbits; the mission lasts 147 hours (December 21-27).

1969   The flight on January 15 of Soyuz 4, carrying Vladimir Shatalov and Boris Volynov, and Soyuz 5, with Aleksei Yeliseyev and Yevgeny Khrunov, marks the first rendezvous in space of two manned vehicles. Two crew members of Soyuz 5 walk in space and join the lone pilot in Soyuz 4.

The Apollo 9 mission, March 3-13, with James A. McDivitt, David R. Scott, and Russell Schweickert, completes the first test in space of the lunar "taxi" operations of staging and docking during 151 earth orbits.

Apollo 10, carrying Tom P. Stafford, John W. Young, and Eugene A. Cernan, undertakes an eight-day mission to the moon May 18, including descent of the taxi to within 9.7 miles of the lunar surface.

Glossary

ABORT: the deliberate interruption of a spaceflight before its mission has been completed.

APOGEE: the highest point reached by a vehicle in orbit.

APOLLO, PROJECT: the U.S. program designed to land a man on the moon; named after the Greek god of light, twin brother of the moon goddess.

ASCENT STAGE: the portion of the lunar "taxi" that carries two astronauts back to the orbiting Apollo.

ASTEROIDS: minor planets which revolve around our sun.

ASTRONAUT: a man who flies space missions.

ASTRONAUTICS: the science of designing, building, and operating spacecraft.

ATMOSPHERE: the mixture of gases, several hundred miles deep, that surrounds the earth:

AXIS: the straight line about which a body rotates.

BALLISTICS: the science of objects hurled into flight—their design, motion, and behavior.

"BARBER CHAIR": the nickname for an astronaut's adjustable seat.

BIRD: the nickname for a rocket or missile.

BOOSTER: the rocket that produces the main propulsion for a spaceflight.

BURN: the firing of a rocket engine during flight.

BURNOUT: the point at which a rocket engine has used up its fuel.

CAPSULE: a cabin designed for spaceflight, sealed and pressurized so that men and equipment can function safely.

CELESTIAL GUIDANCE: the navigation of a spacecraft by reference to the sun, moon, and stars.

CELESTIAL MECHANICS: the study of the motions of heavenly bodies under the influence of gravity.

CLUSTER: two or more rocket engines grouped to act as a unit.

COMMAND MODULE: the part of the Apollo spacecraft that carries three astronauts.

COMMUNICATIONS SATELLITE: any orbiting vehicle that relays signals between ground stations.

COMPONENT: a complete unit within a system that performs one or more given functions.

CONDUCTOR: a substance that readily carries electrical currents.

CONTROL JET (or control rocket): a small rocket that enables a spacecraft to change its direction or speed during flight.

COSMONAUT: a Soviet astronaut.

COUNTDOWN: the system of ticking off the time remaining before a rocket launch.

CSM: the initials for command and service module.

DESCENT STAGE: the part of the lunar taxi containing the descent engine, landing gear, and fuel tanks.

DOCKING: the joining of two spacecrafts after rendezvous.

EARTH SATELLITE: any object that orbits the earth.

ENERGY: the force that enables objects to move or do work.

ESCAPE VELOCITY: the speed an object must reach to overcome the pull of gravity.

EXTRAVEHICULAR ACTIVITY (EVA): the work of astronauts or equipment outside a space vehicle.

FREE FALL: the movement of an object in space traveling without force and meeting no resistance.

FRICTION: the resistance met by all moving objects within our atmosphere.

GEMINI, PROJECT: the U.S. program designed to perfect equipment and techniques, such as rendezvous, needed for a manned lunar landing. Spacecraft used in the program carried two men; named for the twin stars Castor and Pollux.

GRAVITY: the force exerted by a physical object that pulls other objects toward its center; this force gives bodies what we call weight.

GROUND-ELAPSED TIME: during a flight, the amount of time which has passed since lift-off.

GROUND SUPPORT EQUIPMENT: equipment used to service and check out space vehicles.

GUIDANCE: the direction of a space vehicle along a given path.

GUMDROP: the nickname for the command and service modules of Apollo, when they are linked.

GYROSCOPE: an instrument that, like a compass, points in the same direction in space, enabling astronauts to know where they are.

HARDWARE: the finished physical product that emerges after design and construction are completed.

HEAT SHIELD: insulating material that protects a spacecraft from overheating during reentry.

HYDROGEN, LIQUID: hydrogen cooled to at least −423°F. so that its molecules move slowly enough to become liquid.

HYPERGOLIC FUEL: fuel composed of two substances which ignite automatically when they come into contact with each other.

HYPERSONIC: the name for speeds at least 5 times greater than that of sound.

ICBM: intercontinental ballistic missile.

INERTIA: the property of matter which causes it to remain where it is or, if moving, to continue in the same direction at the same speed, unless it is acted upon.

IONOSPHERE: that part of the earth's atmosphere beginning at about 25 miles altitude and extending more than 200 miles. Radio waves may be bounced around the earth using this layer. It reflects them as a mirror does light.

JETTISON: abandon an object from a spacecraft in flight.

LANDER, MOON: a name for the lunar module or LM (pronounced *lem*); also, spider, lunar "taxi." It is the part of the Apollo spacecraft which takes the astronauts to and from the moon.

LASER (light amplification by stimulated emission of radiation): a device that amplifies light by releasing energy stored in matter.

LAUNCH: the takeoff.

LAUNCH PAD: thick concrete base built to support a rocket at takeoff.

LIFT-OFF: the action of a rocket when it takes off straight up from its launch pad.

LIGHT YEAR: a distance equal to about 6 trillion miles.

LM PADS: the circular feet on which the lunar landing module rests.

LUNAR MODULE: see Lander, moon.

MACH NUMBER: the speed of sound through air at any given altitude and temperature.

MAGNETOSPHERE: the magnetic field surrounding earth.

MASS: a measure of the quantity of matter in a body.

MERCURY, PROJECT: the U.S. program designed to place manned capsules into orbit and recover them. Named for the Roman messenger of the gods, noted for his incredible speed.

METEOR: a solid object from space that enters earth's atmosphere.

METEORITE: a meteor that reaches the surface of the earth.

METEOROID: a solid object moving in space.

MICROMINIATURIZATION: the technique of building something in a much smaller size than the original working model.

MISSILE: any object designed to travel through space to a target.

MODULE: a self-contained unit in a spacecraft which serves as a part of the over-all structure. It is usually named for its function, such as "command" module.

MONITOR: to observe.

NASA (National Aeronautics and Space Administration): founded in 1958, this organization handles the research and development for peaceful space activities in the United States.

NUCLEAR PROPULSION: to move something by means of atomic energy.

OXIDIZER: a substance providing oxygen to fuel to make it burn.

OXYGEN, LIQUID: oxygen cooled to at least –279°F. so that its molecules move slowly enough to become liquid.

PAYLOAD: the cargo a rocket carries which is not necessary for flight itself.

PERIGEE: the lowest point reached by a vehicle in earth orbit.

PITCH: up-and-down motion of a vehicle.

PLSS (Portable Life-Support System): the pack carried by astronauts on the moon surface which contains their oxygen, water, and communications equipment.

POUND OF THRUST: the unit of measurement for the force generated by burning gases.

PROPELLANT: a mixture of fuel and oxidizer which burns, producing thrust.

RADAR (Radio Detection and Ranging): a means of locating objects by bouncing radio waves off of them and measuring time elapsed for the echo to return.

REACTION ENGINE: an engine that expels a mixture of hot gases producing thrust in the opposite direction.

RECOVERY: the retrieval of a space vehicle that has completed reentry.

REENTRY: the return of a space vehicle into earth's atmosphere.

RENDEZVOUS: a planned meeting at a preselected time and place between two or more spacecraft.

RETROROCKET: a rocket that fires in the opposite direction to that in which a spacecraft is moving, acting as a brake.

REVOLUTION: the completion of one trip around an orbital path.

ROCKET: any vehicle containing a rocket engine.

SATELLITE: any body given enough speed to go into orbit—a body that revolves around another.

SCRUB: to cancel a scheduled launch.

SEISMOGRAPH: an instrument to record earth tremors.

SENSIBLE ATMOSPHERE: atmosphere extending up to altitudes attainable by aircraft—approximately 100,000 feet.

SERVICE MODULE: in Apollo, the module containing rocket engines, propellants, environmental-control systems, communication and navigation equipment for astronauts.

SEXTANT: an instrument used for measuring positions of stars as aids to navigation.

SOFT LANDING: landing a spacecraft at a slow enough speed to avoid damage.

SOLAR WIND: electrically charged particles flowing from the sun at the rate of several hundred miles per second.

SPACE: the universe beyond earth's atmosphere.

SPACE AGE: an age of exploration which began on October 4, 1957, when the USSR launched Sputnik 1.

SPACE LABORATORY: any space vehicle, manned or unmanned, which carries instruments for obtaining information in space.

SPACE PROBES: spacecraft shot deep enough into space to escape gravitational pull of the earth. Probes may be lunar, planetary, or deep-space, depending on their mission.

SPACE STATION: any orbiting vehicle that may be used to aid space exploration or travel.

STAGING: the planned separation of rocket stages during flight.

SUPERSONIC: the name for speeds faster than that of sound.

TAKEOFF: the launch of a spacecraft.

TELEMETRY: the science of taking electronic measurements during flight and transmission of results to a home base.

TERMINATOR: the line between light and darkness on the moon's surface.

THROTTLE: an instrument used to control speed, such as the accelerator in a car.

THRUST: the force developed by a rocket engine.

TRACKING: the process of following the movement of a spacecraft during its flight.

TRACKING STATION: a station set up to trail an object through space.

TRAJECTORY: a path through space.

TUMBLING: end-over-end motion of a vehicle in flight.

VAB (Vehicle Assembly Building): the place where the Saturn 5 and Apollo components are put together at Cape Kennedy.

VAN ALLEN RADIATION BELTS: two layers of high-energy particles in the earth's magnetosphere.

VELOCITY: Speed.

YAW: side-to-side motion of a vehicle.

ZERO GRAVITY: the point at which weightlessness occurs.

Index

PHOTO CREDITS